Homework

joy 4

이종저

POLY BOOKS

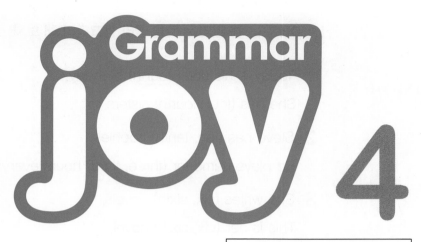

Guide to Use This Homework

Homework는 누적Test를 통하여 이미 학습한 내용을 확실하게 다지는 것을 목표로 합니다. 예를 들면, Uint03의 학습이 끝난 후에는 Unit01과 Unit02를, Unit04의 학습이 끝난 후에는 Unit02와 Unit03을 풀어감으로써 각Unit 마다 추가적으로2회의 복습이 이루어지게 됩니다.

단, Unit07과 Unit08은 Review test를 통하여 2회 복습하도록 구성되어 있습니다.

POLY BOOKS

novel 소설
lay an egg 알을 낳다
raise 기르다

01. 다음 중 알맞은 것을 골라 동그라미 해 보자.

1 Today is his (four, (fourth)) birthday.

She has (four, fourth) sisters.

2 Steve has (ten, tenth) trophies.

He plays game for (three, third) hours everyday.

3 She writes (six, sixth) novels.

This is her (six, sixth) novel.

4 My hen lays (three, third) eggs.

I fry (one, the first) egg every morning.

5 My father raises (twenty, twentieth) cows.

He sells (seven, seventh) cows every year.

02. 다음 빈칸에 주어진 숫자를 영어로 써 보자.

trip 여행
Taiwan 대만
postcard 우편엽서
England 영국

1 I have   two   dogs. (2)

2 This is my   trip to Taiwan. (10)

3 Winter is   season of the year. (4)

4 His house is on   floor. (5)

5 She writes   postcards. (25)

6 The family welcomes   pet. (9)

7 We visited England   times.(14)

01. 다음 중 알맞은 것을 골라 동그라미 해 보자.(두개 가능)

1 2014 (two thousand fourteen, two thousands fourteen)

6월 8일 (eight June, June eight, the eighth of June)

1913년 3월 5일 (March five nineteen thirteen,

five March nineteen thirteen)

1958년 5월 7일 화요일 (Tuesday May seventh nineteen fifty—eight,

May seventh nineteen fifty—eight Tuesday)

7월 6일 목요일 (July sixth Thursday, Thursday July sixth)

2 02—406—xxxx (oh two four zero six ∼, zero two four oh six ∼)

3 $24.16 (twenty four dollar sixteen cent,

twenty four dollars sixteen cents)

4 19.25 (nineteen point two five, nineteen point twenty five

46.87 (four six point eight seven, forty—six point eight seven)

5 2/3 (two three, two third, two thirds)

1/2 (a half, one second, first second)

1/4 (a quarter, one fourth, first fourth)

3/5 (three five, three fifth, three fifths)

3/4 (three fourth, three fourths, three quarters)

7과 5/6 (seven and five sixth, seventh and five sixth,

seven and five sixths)

01. 다음 빈칸에 주어진 숫자를 영어로 써 보자.

salesman 판매원
sell-sold 팔다
fill 채우다
hire 고용하다
play 연극
boring 지루한
starve 굶주리다
director 감독
film 영화
competition 경쟁
runner 경주자
stadium 경기장
tripped 발을 헛딛다

1 Twenty-three doctors work for the hospital.(23)

2 There are   roses in the vase.(12)

3 It is my   house.(2)

4 He met Ann for   time two years ago.(1)

5 The salesman sold   computers.(15)

6 The hotel has   rooms.(70)

7 She filled   bowl with hot water.(6)

8 My boss hired   young men.(100)

9   of the play is too boring.(5)

10 A lot of babies are starving in   world.(3)

11 The director will make   film.(11)

12 This is   competition.(30)

13 There are   soldiers in this camp.(10)

14   runner is coming to the stadium.(8)

15 The man tripped on   stair.(9)

01. 다음 빈칸에 주어진 숫자를 영어로 써 보자.

August 8월
December 12월
October 10월
Thursday 목요일

1 1953년   nineteen fifty−three

2 26.78

3 3과 1/3

4 010 − 679 ∼

5 $15.45

6 5/8

7 8월 4일 금요일

8 17.19

9 2010년

10 8과 3/4

11 12월 25일

12 1/2

13 $92.37

14 9와 3/7

15 2035년 10월 9일 목요일

January 1월
fall 가을

01. 다음 알맞은 것을 골라 동그라미 해 보자.

1 (How, (What)) month is it?   — It is January.

2 What (day, date, time) is it?   — It's Thursday.

3 What (day, date, year) is it?   — It's 1984.

4 What is the (day, date, time) today?   — It's June 15, 2002.

5 (How, What) is the weather?   — It is windy.

6 Do you have (time, the time)?   — It's 3:30.

7 What (day, season, year) is it?   — It's fall.

02. 다음 대답에 알맞은 질문을 써 보자.

foggy 안개낀

1 A: What season   is it?

   B: It's spring.

2 A: is it?

   B: It's July 7.

3 A: What's the weather   ?

   B: It's foggy.

4 A: What time   you   ?

   B: It's a quarter after eight.

5 A: What's   ?

   B: It's ten past two.

01. 다음 빈칸을 숫자로 채우고 ( ) 안에서 알맞은 말을 골라 보자.

1 It's three fifteen.　　　3 시 15 (분, 분 전)입니다.

2 It's four oh two.　　　　□ 시 □ (분, 분 전)입니다.

3 It's five to six.　　　　□ 시 □ (분, 분 전)입니다.

4 It's a quarter to eight.　　□ 시 □ (분, 분 전)입니다.

5 It's midnight.　　　　□ 시 (자정, 정오)입니다.

6 It's half past six.　　　□ 시 □ (분, 분 전)입니다.

7 It's a quarter after eight.　　□ 시 □ (분, 분 전)입니다.

02. 다음 주어진 시각을 영어로 나타낼 때 빈칸을 알맞게 써 보자.

1 12시 15분　twelve fifteen

　　　a quarter past twelve

2 7시 9분　seven □ nine

　　　□ □ seven

3 1시 52분　one □

　　　fifty-two □ one

　　　□ to □

4 3시 30분　□ thirty

　　　□ past three

5 5시 40분　five □

　　　□ □ six

6 4시 45분　four □

　　　a quarter □ □

01. 다음 주어진 문장과 같은 표현을 써 보자.

What time is it?

=   What's the time   ?

=   ?

=   ?

02. 다음 대화의 빈칸에 알맞은 말을 써 보자.

freezing 꽁꽁 얼게 추운
March 3월
February 2월

1   What time   is it?   — It is a quarter to eleven.

2   is the weather?

         is the weather   ? — It's freezing.

3   is it?   — It's Tuesday.

4   is it?   — It's the frist of March.

5   is it?   — It is spring.

6   is it?   — It's February.

7   is it?   — It is 2000.

03. 다음 물음에 알맞은 대답을 써 보자.

Do you have time?   — No,   . I am very busy.

01. 다음 주어진 시각을 영어로 나타낼 때 빈칸을 알맞게 써 보자.

1 7시 5분　seven　_oh_　five

five　after　_seven_

five　_past_　_seven_

2 9시 12분　＿＿＿　twelve

twelve　＿＿＿　nine

twelve　＿＿＿　nine

3 2시 50분　two　＿＿＿

ten to　＿＿＿

4 10시 15분　ten　＿＿＿

a quarter　＿＿＿　ten

＿＿＿　after ten

5 11시 30분　＿＿＿　thirty

＿＿＿　past　＿＿＿

6 6시 정각　six　＿＿＿

02. 다음 주어진 시각을 바꿔쓰고 영어로 나타내보자.

1 03 : 40 ＝ _4_ 시 _20_ 분전

three forty

＝ _twenty to four_

2 01 : 50 ＝ ＿ 시 ＿ 분전

＿＿＿＿

＝ ＿＿＿＿

3 11 : 15

＿＿＿＿

＝ ＿＿＿＿

4 12: 58 ＝ ＿ 시 ＿ 분전

＿＿＿＿

＝ ＿＿＿＿

5 07: 45 ＝ ＿ 시 ＿ 분전

＿＿＿＿

＝ ＿＿＿＿

6 06 : 30

＿＿＿＿

＝ ＿＿＿＿

choose 고르다, 선택하다

01. 주어진 동사의 과거형을 써 보자.

1	say	said	2	break	
3	carry		4	stand	
5	wear		6	take	
7	choose		8	have	
9	draw		10	run	
11	speak		12	swim	
13	sell		14	cost	

02. 주어진 문장을 과거형으로 알맞게 바꿔 보자.

banker 은행원
a lot 많이
mop 대걸레로 닦다
go on a trip 여행가다

1 She is a nurse.

→She   was   a nurse.

2 The bankers are kind.

→The bankers   kind.

3 He hits golf balls a lot.

→He   golf balls a lot.

4 Tony mops the floor in his office.

→Tony   the floor in his office.

5 My mother goes on a trip to New York on her birthday.

→My mother   on a trip to New York on her birthday.

01. 문장의 시제를 고르고 be동사를 우리말에 알맞게 바꿔 보자.

good-looking 잘생긴
neighbor 이웃
popular 인기있는

1 I ___was___ born in England. (현재, (과거))
나는 영국에서 태어났다.

2 They ___ very good-looking. (현재, 과거)
그들은 매우 잘 생겼었다

3 My neighbors ___ kind to me. (현재, 과거)
나의 이웃들은 나에게 친절하다.

4 Michael Jackson ___ a popular singer. (현재, 과거)
마이클 잭슨은 인기있는 가수였다.

5 Riding a bicycle ___ so much fun. (현재, 과거)
자전거 타는 것은 매우 재있다.

02. 다음 우리말에 알맞은 동사를 골라 동그라미 해 보자.

see a doctor 진찰을 받다

1 She (drops, (dropped)) her favorite mug.
그녀는 그녀가 가장 좋아하는 머그잔을 떨어뜨렸다.

2 My cousin (sees, saw) a doctor.
나의 사촌은 진찰을 받았다.

3 The boy (breaks, broke) the window with a ball.
그 소년은 공으로 창문을 깨뜨렸다.

4 We always (win, won, is winning) all the games.
우리는 항상 모든 게임을 이긴다.

5 Some leaves (fall, fell, are falling) down on the ground.
약간의 잎들이 땅에 떨어진다.

01. 다음 주어진 동사를 우리말에 알맞게 바꿔보자.

sandwich 샌드위치
temple 절, 사원
~ ago ~전에
rub 문지르다
belly 배

1 It _____ was _____ sunny yesterday.(be)
어제는 날이 화창했다.

2 I usually _____ a sandwich for breakfast.(eat)
나는 보통 아침으로 샌드위치를 먹는다.

3 She _____ to the temple on Sundays.(go)
그녀는 일요일마다 절에 갔다.

4 We _____ in China last month.(be)
우리는 지난달 중국에 있었다.

5 His father sometimes _____ to the radio in his car.(listen)
그의 아버지는 가끔 그의 차에서 라디오를 들으신다.

6 They _____ here two weeks ago.(come)
그들은 2주 전에 여기로 왔다.

7 My teacher _____ me to the class.(introduce)
나의 선생님은 나를 반에 소개하셨다.

8 Mr. Park _____ many countries last year.(visit)
Mr. Park은 작년에 많은 나라들을 방문했다.

9 My aunt _____ me a nice bicycle.(buy)
나의 고모는 나에게 멋진 자전거를 사 주셨다.

10 Alissa _____ in her baby's belly.(rub)
Alissa는 그녀의 아기의 배를 문질렀다.

01. 다음 주어진 동사를 우리말에 알맞게 바꿔 보자.

1 The peach ___was___ hard.(be)

그 복숭아는 딱딱했다.

2 He _____ the pictures on the wall this morning.(hang)

그는 그 그림들을 오늘 아침 벽에 걸었다.

3 I _____ a stroll in the garden with my puppy.(take)

나는 나의 강아지와 함께 정원을 산책한다.

4 The salesman _____ the demonstration of cosmetics in her house.(do)

그 판매원은 그녀의 집에서 화장품 시연을 했다.

5 Emily _____ her rings in the dresser drawer.(put)

Emily는 그녀의 반지들을 화장대 서랍에 두었다.

6 She _____ Spanish in our class.(teach)

그녀는 우리 반에서 스페인어를 가르쳤다.

7 Dad _____ his daughter's sleepover party.(permit)

아빠는 그의 딸에 슬립오버 파티를 허락했다.

8 Jeremy and Phillip _____ twins.(be)

Jeremy and Phillip은 쌍둥이였다.

9 The high school students _____ summary for their homework.(write)

고등학교 학생들은 그들의 숙제로 요약을 했다.

10 The barista _____ some coffee for customers.(make)

그 바리스타는 손님에게 약간의 커피를 만들어 준다.

hard 딱딱한
stroll 거닐다, 산책하다
salesman 판매원, 외판원
demonstration 시연
cometic 화장품
sleepover (아이들이나 청소년들이 한집에 모여) 함께 자며 놀기, 밤샘파티
summary 요약, 개요
barista 바리스타

accountant 회계사
married couple 부부

01. 다음 문장을 지시대로 바꿔 보자.

1 I was a sick person.

부정문 _I_ _wasn't_ a sick person.

2 He was an accountant.

의문문 _____ _____ an accountant?

3 They were a married couple.

부정문 _____ _____ a married couple.

take a break
잠시 휴식을 취하다
draw—drew 그리다

02. 다음 문장을 지시대로 바꿔 보자.

1 We wanted to take a break.

부정문 _We didn't want_ to take a break.

2 He drew a picture at the park.

의문문 _____ a picture at the park?

3 It snowed a lot last winter.

부정문 _____ a lot last winter.

professor 교수
tie 넥타이

03. 다음 질문에 대답을 완성해 보자.

1 Was Mrs. Brown your professor? – Yes, _she_ _was_ .

2 Were those your ties? – No, _____ _____ .

surprise 놀라게하다
foreigner 외국인

04. 다음 질문에 대답을 완성해 보자.

1 Did he surprise his wife with a gift? – No, _he_ _didn't_ .

2 Did the foreigner have blue eyes? – Yes, _____ _____ .

01. 다음 문장을 지시대로 바꿔 보자.

1 Sally and Lisa were from London.

의문문 　Were　Sally and Lisa　 from London?

2 There were a lot of grapes in the box.

부정문 　　　　　　　　　 a lot of grapes in the box.

3 The brick looked like chocolate.

의문문 　　　　　　　　　 like chocolate?

4 He gave a hand to the girl.

의문문 　　　　　　　　　 a hand to the girl?

5 They knew about it.

부정문 　　　　　　　　　 about it.

6 A few bats were in the woods.

의문문 　　　　　　　　　 in the woods?

7 Jane changed her clothes quickly.

부정문 　　　　　　　　　 her clothes quickly.

8 Noah stayed up late.

의문문 　　　　　　　　　 late?

9 I was wise at that time.

부정문 　　　　　　　　　 wise at that time.

10 She heard the sound of the sea.

부정문 　　　　　　　　　 the sound of the sea.

be from ~출신이다
brick 벽돌
give a hand 도움을 주다
clothes 옷
quickly 재빨리
stay up late 늦게까지
자지 않고 있다
wise 현명한
sound 소리

price 가격
correct 옳은
daytime 낮
same 같은
Italian 이태리의
stray 길을 잃은,
주인을 잃은
rescue 구조하다
rake 갈퀴질하다
baby-sitter 베이비시터
close 가까운, 친밀한

01. 다음 질문에 대답을 완성해 보자.

1 Was the woman beautiful?   Yes, _she was_ .

2 Did you ask the price?   No, _____ .

3 Did Aaron say to her?   Yes, _____ .

4 Are there blue jeans on the bed?   No, _____ .

5 Is the boy a baseball player?   Yes, _____ .

6 Did they bring a picnic basket?   No, _____ .

7 Is the answer correct?   Yes, _____ .

8 Did you see a rainbow in the daytime?   No, _____ .

9 Were they in the same class?   Yes, _____ .

10 Does Vivian enjoy Italian food?   No, _____ .

11 Did your friend borrow your eraser?   Yes, _____ .

12 Did the man rescue the stray dog?   Yes, _____ .

13 Do they rake the fallen leaves in the yard?   No, _____ .

14 Was the old lady your baby-sitter?   Yes, _____ .

15 Are you close to Jane?   No, _____ .

01. 다음 문장을 지시대로 바꿔 보고 의문문은 대답도 써 보자.

1 The cat is very dirty.

의문문   Is the cat   very dirty? Yes,   it is   .

2 He watched the first Spider—Man movie.

부정문   the first Spider—Man movie.

3 They had wonderful day in Paris.

의문문   wonderful day in Paris? No,   .

4 Belle goes swimming early in the morning.

의문문   swimming early in the morning?

Yes,   .

5 We were involved this group.

부정문   involved this group.

6 The owner considered the customer's opinion.

부정문   the customer's opinion.

7 Your brother lost his laptop in the subway.

의문문   his laptop in the subway? No,   .

8 The student was afraid of the test result.

부정문   afraid of the test result.

9 My mother made some doughnuts for me.

부정문   any doughnuts for me.

10 The reporter took notes in the interview.

의문문   notes in the interview? Yes,   .

owner 주인
involved 관련된
consider 사려(고려)하다
customer 손님, 고객
opinion 의견
laptop 휴대용 컴퓨터
afraid 두려워하는
result 결과
doughnuts 도넛츠
interview 인터뷰
take notes 메모하다

test 3

01. 문장의 시제를 고르고, 우리말에 알맞게 주어진 동사를 바꿔 보자.

1 She   was smiling   at that time.(smile)

그녀는 그 때 웃고 있었다.   (현재진행, 과거, 과거진행)

2 He   a wedding ring.(wear)

그는 결혼반지를 끼고 있다.   (현재진행, 과거, 과거진행)

3 Tim   here last weekend.(stay)

Tim은 지난 주말 여기에 머무르고 있었다.   (현재진행, 과거, 과거진행)

4 We   some question.(ask)

우리는 몇가지 질문을 하고 있는 중이다.   (현재진행, 과거, 과거진행)

5 Mary and Jane   you.(miss)

Mary와 Jane은 너를 그리워하고 있었다.   (현재진행, 과거, 과거진행)

02. 다음 문장을 과거진행형으로 바꿔 보자.

chase 뒤쫓다
sew 바느질하다

1 It is raining.

→ It   was raining   .

2 They chase a black wolf.

→ They   a black wolf.

3 Brian chooses his cap at the shop.

→ Brian   his cap at the shop.

4 I am carrying the watermelon.

→ I   the watermelon.

5 She sews her grandson's jacket.

→ She   her grandson's jacket.

01. 다음 주어진 동사를 이용하여 우리말에 알맞게 써 보자.

villager 마을 사람
shave 면도하다
on the phone 전화로
text 문자를 보내다
non-stop 쉬지 않고

1 A lot of villagers   are looking for   Tommy's dog now.(look for)

지금 많은 마을 사람들이 Tommy의 개를 찾고 있다.

2 My dad   in the bathroom.(shave)

나의 아빠는 욕실에서 면도를 하고 있었다.

3 He   after exercise.(take a bath)

그는 운동이 끝나고 목욕하는 중이다.

4 She   with her best friend on the phone.(chat)

그녀는 그녀의 가장 친한 친구와 전화로 잡담을 하고 있었다.

5 The baby   at me then.(wave)

그 아기는 그 때 나에게 손을 흔들고 있었다.

6 They   this bridge in 2008.(build)

그들은 2008년에 이 다리를 짓고 있었다.

7 Jack   non-stop in class.(text)

Jack은 수업시간에 쉬지 않고 문자를 보내고 있다

8 I   my teacher in front of our classmates then.(copy)

나는 그 때 우리 반 학생들 앞에서 나의 선생님 흉내를 내고 있었다.

9 My sisters   the dinner table.(clear)

나의 여동생들은 저녁식탁을 치우고 있었다.

10 Most of people   around the lake.(walk)

대부분의 사람들이 호수 주위를 걷고 있다.

01. 다음 주어진 동사를 이용하여 우리말에 알맞게 빈칸을 채워 보자.

roast 굽다
turkey 칠면조
arrange 마련하다, 주선하다

1 Dad ___was sleeping___ on the sofa.(sleep)

아빠는 소파에서 자고 있었다.

2 She _____ a turkey on Thanksgiving.(roast)

그녀는 추수감사절에 칠면조를 굽고 있다.

3 They _____ the birthday party.(arrange)

그들은 생일 파티를 준비하고 있었다.

4 Mr. Kim and Mrs Kim _____ their son.(wait for)

Mr. Kim and Mrs Kim은 그들의 아들을 기다리고 있었다.

5 My wife _____ the air-conditioner.(turn on)

나의 아내는 에어컨을 켜는 중이다.

02. 다음 문장을 지시대로 바꿔 보자.

gym 체육관
sink 싱크대
hold 잡다
celebrity 연예인, 유명인

1 My uncle was doing exercise at the gym.

부정문 ___My uncle___ ___wasn't___ ___doing___ exercise at the gym.

2 She was holding her mug in front of the sink.

의문문 _____ her mug in front of the sink?

3 We were working after lunch.

부정문 _____ after lunch.

4 You are sitting next to the celebrity.

의문문 _____ next to the celebrity?

5 They were looking over there.

의문문 _____ over there?

01. 다음 질문에 Yes와 No로 시작하는 대답을 완성해 보자.

1 Was the boy bothering you?　　　Yes, _he was_ .

2 Were you upset?　　　No, _____ .

3 Is your aunt napping now?　　　Yes, _____ .

4 Were Amy and Evan strolling along the beach?

　　　　　　　　　　　　　　　No, _____ .

5 Is the lawyer enthusing at the court?

　　　　　　　　　　　　　　　Yes, _____ .

bother 괴롭히다
upset 속상한
nap 졸다
stroll 거닐다
lawyer 변호사
enthuse 열변을 토하다
court 법정

02. 다음 문장을 지시대로 바꾸고 의문문은 대답도 완성해 보자.

1 My grandmother was getting into a car accident.

부정문 _My grandmother wasn't_ getting into a car accident.

2 They are looking at the electronic board.

의문문 _____ the electronic board?

　　　　　　　　　　　　Yes, _____ .

3 A lot of water is flowing into the house.

부정문 _____ into the house.

4 Eden and Phillip were sending e-mails to their clients.

의문문 _____ e-mails to their clients?

　　　　　　　　　　　　No, _____ .

5 She was chewing gum in class.

부정문 _____ gum in class.

get into~ ~에 처하다
accident 사고
electronic board 전광판
flow 흐르다
client 의뢰인, 고객

test 3

hang 걸다, 매달리다
hanger 옷걸이
zookeeper 동물원 사육사

01. 다음 (   ) 안에서 알맞은 동사를 골라 미래형을 만들어 보자.

1 She (is, (will)) (teaches, (teach)) ice-skating.

2 My cousin (is, will) going to (run, running) to school.

3 They (are, will) going to (swam, swim) in the river.

4 Jackson (is, will) (hang, hanging) a sweater on the hanger.

5 I (am, will) (be, is) a zookeeper.

02. 다음을 will을 이용하여 미래형으로 바꿔 보자.

get a passport
여권을 발급받다
write a song
노래를 작곡하다

1 I get a passport this year.

→ I ___will get___ a passport this year.

2 He writes many songs.

→ He _____ many songs.

3 We are honest people.

→ We _____ honest people.

03. 다음을 be going to를 이용하여 미래형으로 바꿔 보자.

fill out 채우다
application 지원서
form 서식

1 It rains.

→ It ___is going to rain___ .

2 He plays the drum with William.

→ He _____ the drum with William.

3 Jenny fills out the application form.

→ Jenny _____ the application form.

01. 다음 두 문장의 뜻이 같도록 빈칸에 알맞은 말을 써 보자.

1 My family will have supper together.

= My family   is going to have   supper together.

2 He is going to turn off his computer in an hour.

= He _____ his computer in an hour.

3 Helen's parents will arrive at the airport.

= Helen's parents _____ at the airport.

4 They are going to support a new basketball team.

= They _____ a new basketball team.

5 This clerk will bring a cool jumper.

= This clerk _____ a cool jumper.

supper 저녁만찬
turn off 끄다
arrive at ~에 도착하다
support 지원하다, 응원하다
clerk 점원
cool 멋진

02. 다음 시제를 고르고 주어진 단어를 이용하여 우리말에 알맞게 문장을 완성해 보자.

1 Ann   will(is going to) be   a high school student.(be)

Ann은 고등학생이 될 것이다.　　　　　　　　　　(현재, 과거, 미래)

2 It _____ five minutes to pull out some money.(take)

약간의 돈을 인출하는데 5분 걸린다.　　　　　　　(현재, 과거, 미래)

3 A pickpocket _____ her purse at the department store.(take)

어떤 소매치기가 백화점에서 그녀의 지갑을 훔쳐갔다.　　(현재, 과거, 미래)

4 I _____ at the market on my way home.(stop off)

나는 집에 가는 도중에 시장에 들를거야.　　　　　(현재, 과거, 미래)

5 My mom _____ my allowance.(raise)

나의 엄마는 내 용돈을 올려줄 것이다.　　　　　　(현재, 과거, 미래)

high school 고등학교
pickpocket 소매치기
department store 백화점
stop off 잠시 들르다(머무르다)
on one's way 도중에
raise 올리다
allowance 용돈

look around 둘러보다
vacuum 진공청소기로
청소하다
clippers 깎는 도구, 가위
stock 주식

01. 다음 주어진 단어를 이용하여 우리말에 알맞게 문장을 완성해 보자.

1 They will(are going to) look around our school.(look around)

그들은 우리 학교를 둘러 볼 것이다.

2 My son _____ Seoul university next year.(enter)

나의 아들은 내년에 서울대학교에 들어갈 것이다.

3 Bill _____ his car.(vacuum)

Bill은 그의 차를 진공 청소기로 청소했다.

4 Helen _____ her son's hair with clippers.(cut)

Helen은 깎는 도구(가위)로 그녀의 아들의 머리를 자른다.

5 I _____ my stocks tomorrow.(sell)

나는 내일 나의 주식을 팔 것이다.

02. 다음 주어진 문장을 부정문과 의문문으로 바꿔 보자.

set up a shop
사업을 시작하다
driver's license 운전면허
within ～내에

1 He will use a desktop.

부정문   He won't use   a desktop.

의문문   Will he use   a desktop?

2 Tom is going to set up a shop in the downtown.

부정문   _____ a shop in the downtown.

의문문   _____ a shop in the downtown?

3 You are going to get a driver's license within this year.

부정문   _____ a driver's license within this year.

의문문   _____ a driver's license within this year?

01. 다음 문장을 지시대로 바꾸고 의문문은 대답도 완성해 보자.

1 She will take a subway.

부정문 ___She won't take___ a subway.

2 I will leave Rome next month.

의문문 _____ Rome next month? Yes, _____ .

3 They are going to go to the cafeteria in our school.

부정문 _____ to the cafeteria in our school.

4 The concert is going to begin soon.

의문문 _____ soon? No, _____ .

5 He will come along with me.

부정문 _____ with me.

6 Jacob is going to visit the dog shelter with his family.

의문문 _____ the dog shelter with his family?

Yes, _____ .

7 We will travel to Mexico.

부정문 _____ to Mexico.

8 Eric will play soccer till 9.

의문문 _____ soccer till 9? No, _____ .

9 We are going to go camping.

부정문 _____ camping.

10 You are going to be a surgeon.

의문문 _____ a surgeon? Yes, _____ .

Rome 로마
soon 곧
come along 함께 오다
shelter 쉼터
vacation 방학
till ~ 까지
surgeon 외과의사

Michael Jackson 마이클
잭슨

01. 다음 ( ) 안에서 알맞은 감탄사를 골라 보자.

1 (How, What) big the teddy bear is!

2 (How, What) a famous doctor he is!

3 (How, What) soft the cake is

4 (How, What) well Michael Jackson dances!

5 (How, What) delicious food this is!

6 (How, What) an easy exam it is!

7 (How, What) strong the wind is blowing!

02. 주어진 문장을 감탄문으로 바꿀 때, ( ) 안에서 알맞은 것을 골라 보자.

graceful 우아한
necklace 목걸이
Rapunzel 라푼젤
area 지역

1 The skater is very graceful.

= (How, What) graceful the skater is!

2 The diamond necklace is very expensive.

= (How, What) expensive the diamond necklace is!

3 Rapunzel's hair is really long.

= (How, What) long Rapunzel's hair is!

4 It is a very wide area.

= (How, What) a wide area it is!

5 They have very deep and blue eyes.

= (How, What) deep and blue eyes they have.

01. 다음 (　) 안의 단어를 바르게 배열하여 감탄문을 만들어 보자.

character 성격, 캐릭터
unique 독특한
priceless 대단히 귀중한
Orlando Bloom 올란도 블룸
(영화배우)

1 (how, this, is, cute, character)!

→ How cute this character is !

2 (you, idea, a, have, what, unique)!

→ !

3 (the, is, information, priceless, how)!

→ !

4 (what, it, a, is, meal, tasty)!

→ !

5 (Orlando Bloom, handsome, How, is)!

→ !

02. 다음 문장을 감탄문으로 바꿔 쓸 때 빈칸을 알맞은 말로 채워 보자.

quiet 조용한
gentle 점잖은
scary 무서운
snake 뱀
mysterious 기이한
photo 사진

1 It is a very quiet room.

→ What a quiet room it is!

2 The man is very gentle.

→ the man is!

3 Snakes are very scary animals.

→ snakes are!

4 Serena studies very hard.

→ Serena studies!

5 This is a very mysterious photo.

→ this is!

Usain Bolt 우사인 볼트
carpet 카펫
flexible 유연한
messy 지저분한
massive 거대한
lively 활기 넘치는

01. 다음 문장을 감탄문으로 바꿔 보자.

1 She is very tired.

→ How tired she is !

2 It is a very nice weather.

→ !

3 Usain Bolt is a very fast runner.

→ !

4 This carpet is very beautiful.

→ !

5 They are very great scientists.

→ !

6 Jane is a very little girl.

→ !

7 Babies are very flexible.

→ !

8 That is a very messy room.

→ !

9 Those are very massive rocks

→ !

10 These songs are very lively.

→ !

test 2

01. 다음 주어진 단어를 이용하여 우리말에 알맞게 영어로 바꿔 보자.

1 저 궁전은 얼마나 오래되었는지! (old)

How old that palace is !

2 이것은 얼마나 뚱뚱한 고양이인지! (fat)

!

3 그 빌딩들은 얼마나 높은지! (high)

!

4 그는 얼마나 멍청한 사람인지! (stupid)

!

5 그 돌고래들은 얼마나 깊이 잠수하는지! (deep)

!

6 그것들은 얼마나 부지런한 새들인지! (diligent)

!

7 그 음악은 얼마나 신나는지! (exciting)

!

8 그 여배우의 얼굴은 얼마나 작은지! (small)

!

9 이것들은 얼마나 놀라운 이야기들인지! (amazing)

!

10 그것은 얼마나 끔찍한 실수인지! (terrible)

!

palace 궁전
stupid 멍청한
person 사람
dolphin 돌고래
dive 잠수하다
actress 여배우
amazing 놀라운
terrible 끔찍한
mistake 실수

Australia 호주
postpone 미루다
leader 지도자
Nice 니스
(프랑스 남동부의 피한지)
architect 건축가

01. 다음은 부정의문문이다. ( ) 안에서 알맞은 말을 골라 동그라미 해 보자.

1 (Wasn't, Didn't) she wonderful? (Yes, No)~.(She was wonderful.)

2 (Aren't, Don't) you from Australia? (Yes, No)~.(I'm from Russia.)

3 (Don't, Doesn't) he love her? (Yes, No)~.(He loves her.)

4 (Don't, Didn't) they postpone the meeting? (Yes, No)~.
(They postponed the meeting.)

5 (Isn't, Doesn't) this train leave for Paris? (Yes, No)~. (It leaves for Nice.)

6 (Wasn't, Didn't) he a leader in our group? (Yes, No)~.
(He was a leader in our group.)

7 (Didn't, Don't) you want to be an architect? (Yes, No)~.
(I didn't want to be a architect.)

02. 다음 빈칸에 알맞은 말을 써 넣어 부정의문문과 대답을 완성해 보자.

close 가까운
sweet 사랑스러운
pack 싸다, 꾸리다
stuff 물건

1 Can't he ride an oxen? No , he can't .(He can't ride an oxen.)

2 _____ you like coffee? _____ , _____ .(I like coffee.)

3 _____ Elsa and Anna be close sisters?
_____ , _____ .(They will be close sisters.)

4 _____ your children always sweet?
_____ , _____ .(They were always sweet.)

5 _____ she pack her stuff?
_____ , _____ .(She didn't pack her stuff.)

test 2

01. 다음은 부가의문문이다. (   ) 안에서 알맞은 말을 골라 동그라미 해 보자.

1 Andy is an insurance planner, (is, (isn't)) he?

2 Victoria wasn't depressed, (was, isn't) she?

3 You are nervous, (do, aren't) you?

4 They don't have a cat, (do, does) they?

5 He payed attention, (did, didn't) he?

6 Open the window for me, (won't, will) (you, we)?

7 Let's do this, (shall, will) (we, you)?

insurance planner
보험 설계사
depressed 우울한
nervous 긴장한
pay attention 주목하다

02. 다음 빈칸에 알맞은 말을 써 넣어 부가의문문과 대답을 완성해 보자.

1 He is intelligent, ___isn't he___ ? Yes, ___he is___ .

2 You won't write poems, _____ ? No, _____ .

3 The flight attendants served meals, _____ ? Yes, _____ .

4 Stella can earn a lot of money, _____ ? No, _____ .

5 Let's think about it _____ ?

6 The fire fighters were very brave, _____ ?

7 Press the volume up key, _____ ?

poem 시
intelligent 지적인
flight attendant 승무원
serve 제공하다
earn 벌다

01. 다음 빈칸에 알맞은 말을 써 넣어 부정의문문을 완성해 보고 대답도 써 보자.

cinnamon 계피
pancake 팬케익
proud 자랑스러운
underwear 속옷
drawer 서랍

1 He is a new chef.

→ ___Isn't he___ a new chef? No, ___he isn't___ .

2 Mr.Blair worries about his pet.

→ _____ worry about his pet? Yes, _____ .

3 You can find a cinnamon pancake.

→ _____ find a cinnamon pancake? No, _____ .

4 It was windy in Jeju Island.

→ _____ windy in Jeju Island? Yes, _____ .

5 Jane will try to give him a chance.

→ _____ try to give him a chance? No, _____ .

6 The ladies were at the bank.

→ _____ at the bank? Yes, _____ .

7 This clothing store had a CCTV.

→ _____ have a CCTV? Yes, _____ .

8 You are proud of yourself.

→ _____ proud of yourself? Yes, _____ .

9 Their car goes well.

→ _____ go well? No, _____ .

10 There are ten underwears in the drawer.

→ _____ ten underwears in the drawer?

Yes, _____ .

01. 다음 빈칸에 알맞은 말을 써 넣어 부가의문문을 완성해 보고 대답도 써 보자.

1 She eats some bread, <u>doesn't she</u> ? Yes, <u>she is</u> .

2 The girls were joyful, _____ ? No, _____ .

3 You can solve the problem, _____ ? Yes, _____ .

4 He won't help us, _____ ? No, _____ .

5 Alvin isn't an athlete, _____ ? Yes, _____ .

6 Jenny does care about him, _____ ? Yes, _____ .

7 Mr. Lee ignored the warning, _____ ? No, _____ .

8 Keep quite, _____ ?

9 They can't accept my article, _____ ? Yes, _____ .

10 Kimberly is half Korean, _____ ? No, _____ .

11 Let's get on the bus, _____ ?

12 My sisters were gorgeous women,

_____ ? Yes, _____ .

13 People are at the City hall _____ ? Yes, _____ .

14 He will desire for his goal, _____ ? No, _____ .

15 My boyfriend didn't call me late at night,

_____ ? Yes, _____ .

joyful 즐거운
athlete 운동선수
care about ~에 마음을 쓰다
ignore 무시하다
warning 경고
accept 받아들이다
article 글, 기사
half Korean 한국계 혼혈인
gorgeous 아주 멋진
City hall 시청
desire 바라다
goal 목표

Final test 1

01 ③ 02 ④ 03 forty-eight dollars twenty-three cents 04 four sevenths 05 nineteen sixty-five 06 eat → ate 07 ③ 08 ③ 09 past(after),to 10 ② 11 ② 12 ④ 13 ② 14 ④ 15 ⑤ 16 ① 17 ③ 18 ① 19 ① 20 ⑤ 21 ④ 22 How,How 23 ③ 24 ⑤ 25 ②

01 ③의 it은 지시대명사로 쓰였고, 나머지는 모두 날씨, 시간, 거리 등을 나타낼 때 쓰이는 비인칭 주어로 쓰였다.

02 What (a) 형+명+주+동, How+형+주+동

03 화폐단위를 읽을 때는 숫자와 함께 화폐 단위를 읽는다.

04 분수를 읽을 때 앞의 분자는 기수로 읽고 뒤의 분모는 서수로 읽는다. 이때 분자가 2이상일 경우 분모를 복수로 한다.

05 연도를 읽을 때는 두 자리씩 끊어서 읽는다.

08 ③은 '시간 있니?'의 뜻이고, 나머지는 모두 '몇 시니?'의 뜻이다.

09 시간을 나타낼 때 '~후에', '~가 지난'의 의미로 after와 past가 쓰이고 to는 '~전'의 뜻을 가진다.

15 read의 과거형은 read이다.

12 Chris는 he로 받아 주고, 앞의 문장이 긍정이면 뒤의 문장은 부정으로, 앞의 문장이 부정이면 뒤의 문장은 긍정으로 만들어야 한다.

Final test 2

01 ② 02 ②,③ 03 Did he come here yesterday? 04⑤ 05 ⑤ 06 ② 07 ③ 08 ⑤ 09 Tom and Sally weren't dancing in the hall. 10 ① 11 was doing, did, does 12 ④ 13 ③ 14 ⑤ 15 ② 16 ② 17 What a nice jumper Jack is wearing! 18 are going to clean up 19 ③ 20 ⑤ 21 ① 22 Are, am 23 ④ 24 ② 25 ①

03 일반동사 과거형의 의문문은 문두에 Did를 사용하고 뒤에 원형동사를 쓴다.

04 일반동사의 과거형 질문은 문두에 Did로 시작하며, 그에 대한 응답도 인칭에 상관없이 did로 대답한다.

05 will not의 축약형은 won't이다.

07 be going to ~ 구문의 부정문은 be 동사 다음에 not을 써 준다.

08 위의 Are you going to ~는 미래를 묻는 표현이지만 be 동사로 시작되는 질문이므로, 그에 대한 대답도 be 동사로 답한다.

11 How로 시작하는 감탄문의 어순은 「How+형용사+주어+동사」 What으로 시작하는 감탄문의 어순은, 「What + (a/ an) + 형용사 + 명사 + 주어 + 동사」 이다.

12 부정 의문문에 대한 대답이 긍정일 때는 Yes로, 부정일 때는 No로 대답한다.

13 부가의문문의 앞의 문장이 긍정이면 부정의 의문문을, 앞의 문장이 부정이면 긍정의 의문문을 붙이며, 시제를 일치시켜준다.

14 권유문은 뒤에 shall we를 붙여 준다.

17 what으로 시작하는 감탄문은 「What+(a/an)+형용사+명사+주어+동사」 이다.

[after unit2]

test1   p2
01
1.fourth,four 2.ten,three 3.six,sixth 4.three,one/the first
5.twenty,seven
02
1.two 2.tenth 3.the fourth 4.the fifth 5.twenty-five 6.the
ninth 7.fourteen

test2   p3
01
1.two thousand fourteen,June eight,the eighth of June,March
five nineteen thirteen,Tuesday May seventh nineteen
fifty-eight,Thursday July sixth 2.zero two four oh six ~
3.twenty four dollars sixteen cents 4.nineteen point two
five,forty-six point eight seven 5.two thirds,a half,a quarter,one fourth,three fifths,three fourths,three quarters,seven
and five sixths

[after unit3]

test1   p4
01
1.Twenty-three 2.twelve 3.second 4.the first 5.fifteen 6.sev-
enty 7.the sixth 8.one hundred 9.The fifth 10.the third 11.the
eleventh 12.the thirtieth 13.ten 14.The eighth 15.the ninth

test2   p5
1.nineteen fifty-three 2.twenty six point seven eight
3.three and one third 4.zero one oh six seven nine ~
5.fifteen dollars forty-five cents 6.five eighths 7.Fri-
day August four(th) 8.seventeen point one nine 9.two
thousand ten 10.eight and three quarters(fourths)
11.December twenty-fifth,the twenty-fifth of December
12.a(one) half 13.ninety-two dollars thirty-seven cents
14.nine and three sevenths 15.Thursday October
nine(ninth) two thousand thirty- five

test3   p6
01
1.What 2.day 3.year 4.date 5.How 6.the time 7.season
02
1. What season 2.What date 3.like 4.do,have 5.the time

test4   p7
01
1.3,15,분 2.4,2,분 3.6,5,분 전 4.8,15,분 전 5.12,자정 6,6,30,분 7,8,15,분
02
1.twelve,a quarter,past 2.oh,nine,past 3.fifty-two,past,
eight,two 4.three,half 5.forty,twenty,to 6.fourty-five,
to,five

[after unit4]

test1   p8
01
1.What's the time 2.What time do you have 3.Do you
have the time
02
1. What time 2.How,What,like 3.What day 4.What date
5.What season 6.What month 7.What year
03
1.I don't

test2   p9
01
1.oh,five,seven,past,seven 2.nine,past,after 3.fifty,three
4.fifteen,past,a quarter 5.eleven,half,eleven 6.o'clock
02
1.4,20,three forty,twenty to four 2.2,10,one fifty,ten
to two 3.eleven fifteen,a quarter past(after) eleven
4.1,2,twelve fifty-eight,two to one 5.8,15,seven forty-five,a quarter to eight 6.six thirty,half past(after) six

test3   p10
01
1.said 2.broke 3.carried 4.stood 5.wore 6.took 7.chose
8.had 9.drew 10.ran 11.spoke 12.swam 13.sold 14.cost
02
1.was 2.were 3.hit 4.mopped 5.went

test4   p11
01&02
1.was 과거2.were 과거3.are 현재4.was 과거5.is 현재
1.dropped 2.saw 3.broke 4.win 5.fall

[after unit5]

test1   p12
01
1.was 2.eat 3.went 4.were 5.listens 6.came 7.indro-
duced 8.visited 9.bought 10.rubbed

test2   p13
01
1.was 2.hung 3.take 4.did 5.put 6.taught 7.permitted
8.were 9.wrote 10.makes

test3   p14
01&02&03&04
1.I,wasn't 2.Was,he 3.They,weren't
1.We didn't want 2.Did he draw 3.It didn't snow
1.she,was 2.they,weren't
1.he,didn't 2.she/he did

test4   p15
01
1.Were Sally and Lisa 2.There weren't 3.Did the brick
look 4.Did he give 5.They didn't 6.Were a few bats 7.Jane
didn't change 8.Did Noah stay up 9.I wasn't 10.She didn't
hear

[after unit6]

test1   p16
01
1.She was 2.I didn't 3.he did 4.there aren't 5.he is
6.they didn't 7.it is 8.I didn't 9.they were 10.she doesn't
11.he/she did 12.he did 13.they don't 14.she was
15.I'm not

test2   p17
01
1.Is the cat,it is 2.He didn't watch 3.Did they have,they
didn't 4.Does Belle go,she does 5.We weren't 6.The
owner didn't consider 7.Did your brother lose,he didn't
8.The student wasn't 9.My mother didn't make 10.Did
the reporter take,she/he did

test3   p18
01
1.was smiling,과거진행 2.is wearing,현재진행 3.was staying,
과거진행 4.are asking,현재진행 5.were missing,과거진행
02
1.was raining 2.were chasing 3.was choosing 4.was
carrying 5.was sewing
test4   p19
01
1.are looking for 2.was shaving 3.is taking a bath 4.was
chatting 5.was waving 6.were building 7.is texting 8.was
copying 9.were clearing 10.are walking

[after unit7]
test1   p20
01
1.was sleeping 2.is roasting 3.were arranging 4.were
waiting for 5.is turning on
02
1.My uncle,wan't,doing 2.Was,she,holding 3.We,wer-
en't,working 4.Are,you,sitting 5.Were,they,looking
test2   p21
01
1.he was 2.I wasn't 3.she is 4.they weren't 5.she/he is
02
1.My grandmother wasn't 2.Are they looking at,they are
3.A lot of water isn't flowing 4.Were Eden and Phillip
sending,they weren't 5.She wasn't chewing
test3   p22
01
1.will,teach 2.is,run 3.are,swim 4.will,hang 5.will,be
02
1.will get 2.will write 3.will be
03
1.is going to rain 2.is going to play 3.is going to fill out
test4   p23
01
1.is going to have 2.will turn off 3.are going to arrive
4.will spport 5.is going to bring
02
1. will(is going to)be,미래 2.takes,현재 3.took,과거4.will
(am going to)stop off,미래 5.will(is going to) raise,미래

[after unit8]
test1   p24
01
1.will(are going to)look around 2.will(is going to) enter
3.vacuumed 4.cuts 5.will(am going to) sell
02
1.He won't use,Will he use 2.Tom isn't going to set up,Is
Tom going to set up 3.You aren't going to get,Are you
going to get
test2   p25
01
1.She won't take 2.Will you have,I will 3.They aren't going to go 4.Is the concert going to begin,it isn't

5.He won't come along 6.Is Jacob going to visit,he is
7.We won't travel 8.Will Eric play,he won't 9.We aren't
going to go 10.Are you going to be,I am
test3   p26
01&02
1.How 2.What 3.How 4.How 5.What 6.What 7.How
1.How 2.How 3.How 4.What 5.What
test4   p27
01
1.How cute this character is 2.What a unique idea you
have 3.How priceless the information is 4.What a tasty
meal it is 5.How handsome Orlando Bloom is
02
1.What a quiet room 2.How gentle 3.What scary anima
4.How hard 5.What a mysterious photo
[review unit7]
test1   p28
01
1. How tired she is 2.What a nice weather it is 3.What
a fast runner Usain Bolt is 4.How beautiful this carpet is
5.What great scientists they are 6.What a little girl Jane
is 7.How flexible babies are 8.What a messy room that is
9.What massive rocks those are 10.How lively these song
test2   p29
01
1.How old that palace is 2.What a fat cat this is 3.How
high the buildings are 4.What a stupid person he is
5.How deep the dolphins dive 6.What diligent birds the
are 7.How exciting the music is 8.How small the actress
face is 9.What amazing stories these are 10.What a terrible mistake it is
[review unit8]
test1   p30
01&02
1.Wasn't,Yes 2.Aren't,No 3.Doesn't,Yes 4.Didn't,Yes
5.Doesn't, No 6.Wasn't,Yes 7.Didn't,No
1.Can't,No,he can't 2.Don't,Yes,I do 3.Won't,Yes,they will
4.Weren't,Yes,they were 5.Didn't,No,she didn't
test2   p31
01&02
1.isn't 2.was 3.aren't 4.do 5.didn't 6.will,you 7.shall,we
1.isn't he,he is 2.will you,I won't 3.didn't they,they did
4.can't she,she can't 5.Shall we 6.weren't they 7.will you
test3   p32
1.Isn't he,he isn't 2.Doesn't Mr. Blair,he does 3.Can't
you,I can't 4.Wasn't it,it was 5.Won't Jane,she won't
6.Weren't the ladies,they were 7.Didn't this clothing
store,it did 8.Aren't you,I am 9.Doesn't their car,it doesn
10.Aren't there,there are
test4   p33
01
1.doesn't she,she is 2. weren't they,they weren't
3.can't you,I can 4.will he,he won't 5.is he,he is
6.doesn't she,she does 7.didn't he,he didn't 8.will
you 9.can they,they can 10.isn't she,she isn't 11.shall
we 12.weren't they,they were 13.aren't they,they are
14.won't he,he won't 15.did he,he did

Grammar joy 4

저자 **이종저**

이화여자대학교 졸업
Longman Grammar Joy 1, 2, 3, 4권
Longman Vocabulary Mentor Joy 1, 2, 3권
I am Grammar 1, 2권
Grammar & Writing Level A 1, 2권 / Level B 1, 2권
Polybooks Grammar joy start 1, 2, 3, 4권
Polybooks Grammar joy 1, 2, 3, 4권
Polybooks 기본을 잡아주는 중등 영문법 1a,1b,2a,2b,3a,3b권
Polybooks 문법을 잡아주는 영작 1, 2, 3, 4권
Polybooks Grammar joy & Writing 1, 2, 3, 4권
Polybooks Bridging 초등 Voca 1, 2권
Polybooks Joy 초등 Voca 1, 2권

감수 **Jeanette Lee**

Wellesley college 졸업

Grammar **joy** 4

지은이 | 이종저
펴낸곳 | POLY books
펴낸이 | POLY 영어 교재 연구소
기 획 | 박정원
편집디자인 | 이은경
삽화 | 이수진
초판 1쇄 인쇄 | 2015년 4월 25일
초판 21쇄 발행 | 2023년 2월 10일

POLY 영어 교재 연구소
경기도 성남시 분당구 황새울로 200번길 28 1128호
전화 070-7799-1583
ISBN | 979-11-86924-25-9
         979-11-86924-23-5(set)

Grammar joy 4

Preface

그 동안 Grammar Mentor Joy에 보내 주신 아낌없는 사랑과 관심에 힘입어 저자가 직접 Grammar Joy 시리즈의 개정판을 출간하게 되었습니다. 이에 더욱 학생들의 효과적인 학습에 도움이 될 수 있도록 연구개발하여 새롭게 선보이게 되었습니다.

영어 문법을 쉽고 재미있게 가르치고 배우길 바라며

본 개정판은 이전 학습자 및 선생님들의 의견과 영어 시장의 새로운 흐름에 맞춰 현장 교육을 바탕으로 집필하였습니다.

Grammar Joy는 다년간 현장 교육을 바탕으로, 학생의 눈높이와 학습 패턴에 맞춘 개념 설명, 재미있고 능동적이며 반복학습을 통해 자신도 모르는 사이에 영어 어휘와 문법을 익혀 나갈 수 있도록 합니다.

기본기를 확실히 다지도록 합니다

학생들은 대체로, 처음엔 영어에 흥미를 가지다가도 일정 시간이 흐르면 점차 어려워하고 지겹게 느끼기 시작합니다. 하지만, 기본 실력을 다지고 어느 정도 영어에 흥미를 계속 유지하도록 지도하면 어느 순간 실력이 월등해지고 재미를 붙여 적극성을 띠게 되는 것이 영어 학습입니다. Grammar Joy는 영어 학습에 꾸준히 흥미를 가질 수 있도록 기본기를 다져 줍니다.

어려운 정통 문법은 나중으로 미룹니다

영어에도 공식이 있습니다. 물론 실력자들은 공식이 아니라 어법이라고 하지요. 하지만 처음부터 어려운 어법을 강요하기보다는 쉬운 수학문제처럼, 어휘의 활용과 어순을 쉽게 이해할 수 있도록 규칙적인 해법을 공식화할 필요가 있습니다. 매우 단순해 보이지만 이를 반복 학습하다보면 어느새 공식의 개념을 깨닫게 되고 나중엔 그 공식에 얽매이지 않고 스스로 활용할 수 있게 됩니다. 이 책에서 쉬운 문제를 집중해서 푸는 것이 바로 그 공식을 소화해 가는 과정이라고 할 수 있습니다.

생동감있는 다양한 문장들로 이루어져 있습니다

실생활에서도 자주 쓰이는 문장들로 구성하여 현장 학습효과를 낼 수 있도록 하였습니다.

최고보다는 꼭 필요한 교재이고자 합니다

다년간 현장 교육을 통해, 학생들이 기존 문법 체계에 적응하기 어려워한다는 사실을 발견하였습니다. 학생들의 눈높이에 맞춰 흥미로운 학습 내용을 다루면서 자연스럽게 문법과 연계되는 내용들을 다루었습니다. 특히 이번 개정판은 기본을 잡아주는 중등 영문법(Grammar Joy Plus)와 연계하여 중학교 내신에 대비에 부족함이 없도록 내용을 구성하였으므로 Grammar Joy를 끝내고 기본을 잡아주는 중등 영문법(Grammar Joy Plus)를 공부한다면, 쓸데없는 중복 학습을 피하고 알찬 중학과정의 grammar 까지 완성할 수 있을 것이라 믿습니다.

모쪼록, 이 교재를 통해 선생님과 학생들이 재미있고 흥미있는 학습으로 소기의 성과를 얻을 수 있기를 기대하며 그동안 이번 시리즈를 출간하느라 함께 이해하며 동행해 주었던 이은경님께 아울러 감사드립니다.

저자 이종저

Contents

Series Contents

Guide to This Book

1 Unit별 핵심정리

가장 기초적인 문법 사항과 핵심 포인트를 알기 쉽게 제시하여 주의 환기 및 개념 이해를 돕습니다.

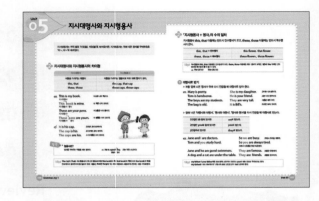

2 기초 다지기

Unit별 핵심 내용에 대한 매우 기초적인 확인 문제로, 개념 이해 및 스스로 문제를 풀어 보는 연습을 할 수 있도록 합니다.

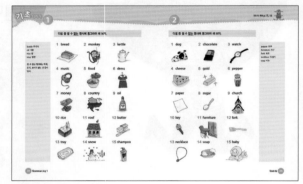

3 꼭꼭 다지기

기초 다지기보다 다소 난이도 있는 연습문제로, 앞서 배운 내용을 복습할 수 있도록 합니다.

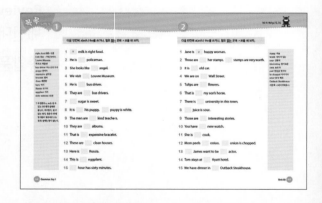

4 실력 다지기

다양한 형태로 제시되는 확장형 응용문제를 통해 문법 개념을 확실히 이해하고 실력을 굳힐 수 있도록 합니다.

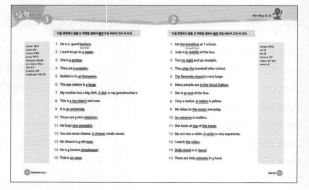

5 실전 테스트

Unit별 마무리 테스트로서, 해당 Unit에서 배운 모든 문법 개념이 적용된 문제 풀이를 통해 응용력을 키우고 학교 선행학습에 대비할 수 있도록 합니다.

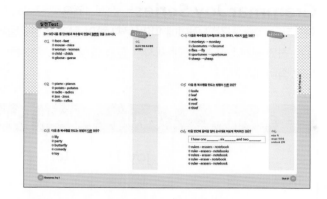

6 Quiz

한 Unit이 끝난 뒤에 쉬어가는 페이지로서, 앞서 배운 내용을 퀴즈 형태로 재미있게 풀어보고 다음 Unit로 넘어갈 수 있도록 합니다.

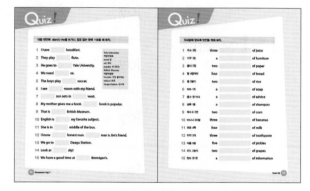

7 Review 테스트, 내신 대비

그 동안 배운 내용을 다시 한 번 복습할 수 있도록 이미 학습한 Unit에 대한 주관식 문제와 내신 대비를 위한 객관식 문제들을 풀어 보도록 합니다.

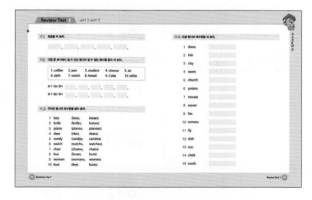

8 종합문제

최종 마무리 테스트로서, Unit 1~8 전체에 대한 종합적인 학습 내용을 다시 한번 점검하고 취약 부분을 파악할 수 있도록 합니다.

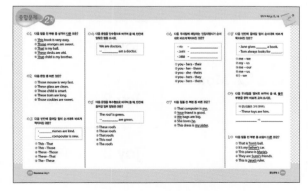

How to Use This Book

Grammar Joy Series는 전체 4권으로 구성되었으며, 각 권당 6주, 총 6개월의 수업 분량으로 기획되었습니다. 학습자와 학습 시간의 차이에 따라 문제 풀이 단계가운데 일부를 과제로 부여하거나 보충 수업을 통하여 시수를 맞출 수 있도록 하였습니다. 또한, 아래 제시된 진행 방식 외에, 학생들이 취약한 학습 영역을 다룬 교재를 먼저 채택하여 수업하실 수도 있습니다.

Month	Course	Week	Hour	Curriculum (Unit)	Homework/ Extra Curriculum
1st Month	Joy 1	1st	1 2 3	**1.** 셀 수 있는 명사	▶각 Unit별 퀴즈 ▶시수별 단어 풀이 과제 부여 또는 수업 중 단어 실력 테스트 ▶Review Test 내신대비
	Joy 1	2nd	1 2 3	**2.** 셀 수 없는 명사 **3.** 관사	
	Joy 1	3rd	1 2 3	**4.** 인칭대명사와 지시대명사	
	Joy 1	4th	1 2 3	**5.** 지시대명사와 지시형용사	
2nd Month	Joy 1	1st	1 2 3	**6.** 인칭대명사의 격변화 **7.** be동사의 긍정문	
	Joy 1	2nd	1 2 3	**8.** be동사의 부정문, 의문문	
	Joy 2	3rd	1 2 3	**1.** There is~/There are~ **2.** 일반동사의 긍정문	▶각 Unit별 퀴즈 ▶시수별 단어 풀이 과제 부여 또는 수업 중 단어 실력 테스트 ▶Review Test 내신대비
	Joy 2	4th	1 2 3	**3.** 일반동사의 부정문과 의문문	
3rd Month	Joy 2	1st	1 2 3	**4.** 현재진행형	
	Joy 2	2nd	1 2 3	**5.** 형용사	
	Joy 2	3rd	1 2 3	**6.** some, any와 many, much, a lot of **7.** 부사	
	Joy 2	4th	1 2 3	**8.** 비교	

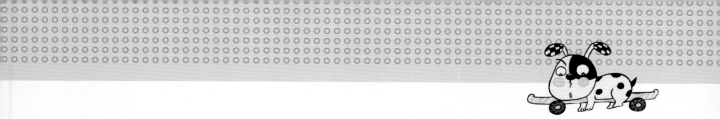

Month	Course	Week	Hour	Curriculum (Unit)	Homework/Extra Curriculum
4th Month	Joy 3	1st	1 2 3	**1.** 「의문사 + 일반동사」 의문문 **2.** 「의문사 + be동사」 의문문	▶각 Unit별 퀴즈 ▶시수별 단어 풀이 과제 부여 또는 수업 중 단어 실력 테스트 ▶Review Test 내신대비
	Joy 3	2nd	1 2 3		
	Joy 3	3rd	1 2 3	**3.** 의문대명사와 의문형용사 **4.** 의문부사(1)	
	Joy 3	4th	1 2 3	**5.** 의문부사(2) **6.** 접속사와 명령문	
5th Month	Joy 3	1st	1 2 3	**7.** 조동사(can, must)	
	Joy 3	2nd	1 2 3	**8.** 전치사	
	Joy 4	3rd	1 2 3	**1.** 기수, 서수 **2.** 비인칭주어	▶각 Unit별 퀴즈 ▶시수별 단어 풀이 과제 부여 또는 수업 중 단어 실력 테스트 ▶Review Test 내신대비 ▶종합문제
	Joy 4	4th	1 2 3	**3.** be동사, 일반동사 과거형의 긍정문	
6th Month	Joy 4	1st	1 2 3	**4.** 과거형의 부정문, 의문문	
	Joy 4	2nd	1 2 3	**5.** 과거진행형	
	Joy 4	3rd	1 2 3	**6.** 미래형 **7.** 감탄문	
	Joy 4	4th	1 2 3	**8.** 부정의문문, 부가의문문	

Knowledge is Power.

Unit 01

기수, 서수

나이나 개수 등을 말할 때 쓰는 수를
기수라고 하고, 순서나 차례를 나타낼 때
쓰는 수를 서수라고 한다.

기수, 서수

기수, 서수란?

기수란 하나, 둘, 셋, …과 같이 나이, 개수 등을 말할 때 쓰는 수를 말하고, 서수란 첫째, 둘째, 셋째, …와 같이 순서, 차례를 나타낼 때 쓰는 수를 말한다.

 기수와 서수

서수 앞에는 **the**가 온다.

ex. He is **the first** visitor. 그는 첫 번째 방문객이다.

기수		서수	
1	one	1st	first
2	two	2nd	second
3	three	3rd	third
4	four	4th	fourth
5	five	5th	fifth
6	six	6th	sixth
7	seven	7th	seventh
8	eight	8th	eighth
9	nine	9th	ninth
11	eleven	11th	eleventh
12	twelve	12th	twelfth
14	fourteen	14th	fourteenth
15	fifteen	15th	fifteenth
18	eighteen	18th	eighteenth
19	nineteen	19th	nineteenth
20	twenty	20th	twentieth
21	twenty-one	21st	twenty-first
22	twenty-two	22nd	twenty-second
30	thirty	30th	thirtieth
40	forty	40th	fortieth
50	fifty	50th	fiftieth
90	ninety	90th	ninetieth
100	one hundred	100th	one hundredth

② 기수와 서수를 이용한 숫자 읽기

① 연도 : 보통 두 자리씩 끊어 읽는다.

ex. 1969년 : nineteen(19) sixty-nine(69)

2004년 : two thousand four = twenty oh four

2014년 : two thousand fourteen = twenty fourteen

Tip!
1. '~월 ~일'은 우리말과 어순이 같으며 한 덩어리로 묶어서 함께 다닌다고 생각한다.
2. 작은 단위부터 나타낸다.

② 년/월/일/요일 : 요일과 달은 첫 글자를 대문자로 표시한다.

▶ **월/일**

ex. 3월 6일 : **March six(sixth)**

of를 사용하면 날짜를 'the＋서수'로 표시하며 '일(the＋서수)＋of＋월'의 순서로 나타낸다.

ex. 3월 6일 : March six(sixth) = **the sixth of** March

▶ **년/월/일**

ex. 2014년 3월 6일 : March six two thousand fourteen

▶ **년/월/일/요일**

ex. 2014년 3월 6일 일요일 : **Sunday** March six two thousand fourteen

③ 전화번호 : 한 자리씩 기수로 읽는다. 0이 맨 처음에 올 때는 **zero**로 읽는다.

ex. 031-249-5301 : **zero** three one two four nine five three **oh** one

④ 소수 읽기 : 소수점 앞은 기수로 읽고, 소수점은 '**point**' 라고 읽는다. 소수점 이하는 기수로 한 자리씩 읽는다.

ex. 13.75 : **thirteen point** seven five

⑤ 돈 : 숫자와 함께 화폐 단위를 읽는다.

ex. $43.17 : **forty three dollars (and)** seventeen cents

⑥ 분수 읽기 : 분자부터 읽고 분모를 읽는다. 분자는 기수로, 분모는 서수로 읽는다. 분자가 2 이상이면 분모는 복수형(-s)를 붙여 읽는다.

ex. $\frac{1}{2}$: a/one half $\qquad\qquad$ $\frac{1}{3}$: a/one third

$\frac{2}{3}$: two thirds $\qquad\qquad$ $\frac{1}{4}$: a/one quarter, a/one fourth

$\frac{3}{4}$: three fourths, three quarters $\qquad$ $2\frac{3}{7}$: two **and** three sevenths

다음 빈칸에 기수를 쓰고, 알맞은 서수를 골라 동그라미 해 보자.

1	1	*one*	(oneth, (first))
2	2	two	(twoth, second)
3	3	three	(third, threeth)
4	4	four	(forth, fourth)
5	5	five	(fiveth, fifth)
6	9	nine	(ninth, nineth)
7	11		(eleventh, eleveth)
8	12		(twelveth, twelfth)
9	14		(fourteenth, forteenth)
10	15		(fifteenth, fiveteenth)
11	20		(twentyth, twentieth)
12	21	twenty-one	(twentieth-first, twenty-first)
13	22		(twentieth-two, twenty-second)
14	30		(thirtieth, thirtith)
15	33	thirty-three	(thirtith-third, thirty-third)

2 다음 빈칸에 기수를 쓰고, 알맞은 서수를 골라 동그라미 해 보자.

1 40 *forty* (fortyth, (fortieth))

2 44 forty-four (forty-fourth, fortieth-four)

3 45 (fortieth-fifth, forty-fifth)

4 50 (fiftieth, fifteth)

5 51 fifty-one (fiftieth-one, fifty-first)

6 54 (fifty-forth, fifty-fourth)

7 55 fifty-five (fiftieth-fifth, fifty-fifth)

8 60 sixty (sixtith, sixtieth)

9 69 sixty-nine (sixtieth-nineth, sixty-ninth)

10 70 seventy (seventieth, seventyth)

11 72 seventy-two (seventieth-two, seventy-second)

12 80 (eightieth, eighteth)

13 88 (eighty-eightth, eighty-eighth)

14 90 (ninetith, ninetieth)

15 100 (one hundredth, first hundred)

다음 중 알맞은 말을 골라 동그라미 해 보자.

wedding day 결혼기념일
book report 독후감
chance 기회
text message 문자 메세지
visa 비자
middle school 중학교

1 Today is my (ten, (tenth)) wedding day.

Mom looks (ten, tenth) younger.

2 This is his (six, sixth) book report.

I visited here (six, sixth) times.

3 Jim has (four, fourth) chances.

Jim has the (four, fourth) chance.

4 She has (third, three) children.

The baby is her (third, three) child.

5 He scored (second, two) goals.

Korea team scored the (second, two) goal.

6 Take this medicine (thirty, thirtieth) minutes after a meal.

Tom sent to me his (thirty, thirtieth) text message.

7 I got my (five, fifth) visa.

I buy (five, fifth) pencils.

8 We need (one, first) day more.

Tomorrow is the (one, first) day of middle school.

4

다음 중 알맞은 말을 골라 동그라미 해 보자.

1 This is the (nine, ⟨ninth⟩) meeting for him.

2 She is my (one, first) love.

3 Mom usually cooks for (two, second) hours.

4 This is her (six, sixth) trip to America.

5 He passed the exam at the age of (eighteen, eighteenth).

6 I read his (seven, seventh) novel.

7 The (eight, eighth) game is over.

8 He tossed (five, fifth) balls.

9 We lost (eight, eighth) games.

10 I remember (second, two) members in the club.

11 He meets (four, fourth) people.

12 Friday is the (six, sixth) day of the week.

13 The policeman captured (twelve, twelfth) robbers.

14 There are (two, second) different things.

15 This is her (five, fifth) gold medal.

at the age of ~의 나이에
novel 소설
be over 끝나다
lose 지다
lost: lose의 과거
member 구성원
capture 잡다
robber 강도
different 다른
thing 것

다음 중 알맞은 말을 골라 동그라미 해 보자.

1 2013년 (two thousand thirteen, two thousands thirteen)
1851년 (eighteen five one, eighteen fifty-one)

2 6월 18일 (eighteen June, June eighteen)
1945년 8월 8일 목요일
(thursday August eight nineteen forty-five,
Thursday August eight nineteen forty-five)

3 064- 7815-xxxx (oh six four seven eight one five-,
zero six four seven eight one five-)
1544-1205-xxxx (one five four four one two oh five-,
one five four four twelve oh five-)

4 45.62 (four five point six two, forty-five point six two)
96.39 (ninety-six point three nine,
ninety-six point thirty-nine)

5 $15.82 (fifteen dollar eighty-two cents,
fifteen dollars eighty-two cents)
$96.18 (nine six dollars eighteen cents,
ninety-six dollars eighteen cents)

6 $\frac{1}{2}$ (one two, a half) $\frac{1}{3}$ (first three, one third)
$\frac{2}{3}$ (two third, two thirds) $\frac{1}{4}$ (one quarter, one four)

5 dollar와 cent는 복수일 때 's'가 붙는다.

6

다음 중 알맞은 말을 골라 동그라미 해 보자.

1 1598년 (fifteenth ninety-eight, fifteen ninety-eight)

2011년 (two thousands eleven, twenty eleven)

2 1월 2일 월요일 (Monday January second,

January second Monday)

1918년 3월 5일 화요일

(Tuesday March fifth, nineteen eighteen,

Tuesday nineteen eighteen, March fifth)

3 080-5242-xxxx   (zero eight oh five two four two,

zero eighty fifty-two forty- two)

043- 9826-xxxx   (oh four three nine eight two six,

zero four three nine eight two six)

4 74.89 (seventy-four eighty-nine,

seventy-four point eight-nine)

56.03 (fifty-six point oh three, fifty-sixth point oh three)

5 $26.93 (twenty-six dollar ninety three cent,

twenty-six dollars ninety three cents)

$58.12 (five eight dollars twelve cents,

fifty-eight dollars twelve cents)

6 $\frac{3}{4}$ (three quarters, three-fourth)

$\frac{3}{5}$ (three-fifths, three-fifth)

7 $3\frac{4}{5}$ (three and four-fifths, three four-fifths)

$2\frac{5}{7}$ (two and five-seventh, two and five-sevenths)

1 hundred(백)와 thousand(천)은 복수라도 's'가 붙지 않는다.

5 dollar와 cent는 복수일때 's'가 붙는다.

다음 ( ) 안의 숫자를 기수 또는 서수로 써 보자. (서수 앞에는 the를 붙인다.)

collect 모으다, 수집하다
finger 손가락
floor 층
for ~동안
gate 문
run after ~를 쫓다
deer 사슴
crocodile 악어
peach 복숭아
postcard 우편 엽서

* 서수/기수 사용시,
　단/복수에 주의하자.
ex. the sixth hit song
　　여섯 번째 히트곡
cf. his six hit songs
　　그의 6곡의 히트곡들

1 It is _the sixth_ hit song. (6)

2 I am in _____ grade. (1)

3 She collects _____ erasers. (19)

4 We have _____ fingers. (10)

5 Here is _____ bus stop from my house. (2)

6 He is _____ years old. (7)

7 My office is on _____ floor. (5)

8 He can swim for _____ hours. (3)

9 They pass through _____ gate. (9)

10 The lion runs after only _____ deer. (1)

11 _____ day of the week is Sunday. (1)

12 They have _____ crocodiles. (4)

13 You buy _____ peaches. (10)

14 _____ day of September is my birthday. (7)

15 Tom sends _____ postcards to his friends. (8)

2

다음 ( ) 안의 숫자를 기수 또는 서수로 써 보자. (서수 앞에는 the를 붙인다.)

1 There are _eleven_ oranges in the basket. (11)

2 Push _____ button! (2)

3 She has _____ alarm clocks. (2)

4 _____ day of the week is Tuesday. (3)

5 There are _____ cows in the farm. (12)

6 She chews the gum for _____ minutes. (10)

7 _____ question is very difficult. (6)

8 She is _____ student in this line. (15)

9 You pay _____ dollars for this T-shirt. (10)

10 Christmas is on _____ of December. (25)

11 We plant _____ pine trees. (9)

12 It is his _____ book report. (5)

13 They pass through _____ gates. (7)

14 This is _____ test. (2)

15 They meet at _____ o'clock. (4)

button 단추
alarm clock 자명종
cow 소
chew 씹다
minute 분
question 질문
difficult 어려운
line 선, 줄
pine tree 소나무
book report 독후감

12 소유격이 있을때는
서수라도 the를
붙이지 않는다.

다음 숫자를 영어로 써 보자.

1 $\frac{1}{6}$ one *sixth*

2 1950년   nineteen _____

3 2006년   _____ oh six

4 $10.25   ten dollars _____

5 7월 16일   July _____

6 23.15   twenty three _____

7 $\frac{3}{4}$ three _____

8 $2\frac{3}{4}$ _____ and _____

9 445-5301   four four five _____

10 4월 7일 월요일   _____ April _____

11 $5.00   five _____

12 46.29   _____ point two nine

13 1월 15일   _____ of January

14 $\frac{4}{5}$ four _____

15 2002년 9월 22일   _____ twenty oh two

4

다음 숫자를 영어로 써 보자.

1 46.75

forty-six _point seven five_

2 $100.59

one hundred _____ fifty nine _____

3 5월 27일

_____ of May

4 $\frac{1}{8}$

one _____

5 018-246-xxxx

_____ one eight two four six-xxxx

6 1923년

nineteen _____

7 1993년 12월 5일

December _____ _____

8 18.64

_____ six four

9 $\frac{4}{7}$

four _____

10 3491-2083

three four nine _____ two _____
_____ three

11 72.62

_____ point _____

12 $8\frac{4}{7}$

eight _____ four- sevenths

13 3월 4일 금요일

_____ March _____

14 $60.28

sixty dollars _____

15 $\frac{5}{10}$

_____ - tenths

다음 문장이나 숫자 읽기에서 밑줄 친 부분들 중에서 틀린 곳을 바르게 고쳐 써 보자.

1 I <u>open</u> <u>five</u> box.
    the fifth

2 1995년 : <u>nineteen</u> <u>nine</u> five

3 $\dfrac{1}{4}$: <u>one</u> - <u>forth</u>

4 27.17 : <u>twenty-seven</u> point <u>seventeen</u>

5 He buys <u>second</u> <u>coats</u>.

6 The pet shop is <u>two</u> <u>building</u> next to the hospital.

7 010-4812-6798 : <u>oh</u> one <u>oh</u>, four eight one two,
    six seven nine eight

8 Today is his <u>thirteen</u> <u>birthday</u>.

9 541-7415 : <u>five</u> four one, <u>seventy four fifteen</u>

10 $\dfrac{1}{2}$: <u>one</u> <u>two</u>

11 There are <u>thirtieth</u> <u>people</u> in the pool.

12 $56.15 : <u>fifty-six</u> dollars fifteen <u>cent</u>

13 The <u>three</u> day of this month is <u>Monday</u>.

14 $\dfrac{3}{5}$: <u>three</u> <u>fifth</u>

15 It's <u>third</u> of <u>July</u>.

2

다음 문장이나 숫자 읽기에서 밑줄 친 부분들 중에서 틀린 곳을 바르게 고쳐 써 보자.

1 $30.75 : thirty <u>dollar</u> <u>seventy five</u> cents

dollars

2 82.34 : <u>eighty two</u> point <u>third</u> four

3 539-4724 : five <u>three</u> nine, forty <u>seven</u> <u>two four</u>

4 $\dfrac{1}{2}$: <u>one</u> <u>second</u>

5 48번째 : the <u>fortieth</u> <u>eighth</u>

6 4월 3일 : <u>third</u> of <u>April</u>

7 1447년 : <u>one four</u> <u>forty</u> <u>seven</u>

8 $\dfrac{7}{8}$: <u>seven</u> <u>eighth</u>

9 Tom has <u>sixteenth</u> <u>pencils</u>.

10 2004년 8월 15일 목요일 : <u>August 15 Thursday</u>, <u>2004</u>

11 $6.15 : <u>sixth</u> dollars <u>fifteen</u> cents

12 $2\dfrac{2}{5}$: <u>two</u> and two <u>fifth</u>

13 There are <u>twelfth</u> <u>girls</u> at the taxi stand.

14 1726년 5월 3일 : May <u>third</u>, seventeen <u>twenty-sixth</u>

15 018-246-5703 : <u>zero</u> one eight, two four six,

five seven <u>zero</u> three

01 다음 중 기수와 서수에 관한 설명으로 옳지 <u>않은</u> 것은?

① 순서나 차례 등을 나타낼 때는 서수를 사용한다.
② 서수 앞에는 the를 붙인다.
③ 서수는 몇몇을 제외하고 보통은 '기수 + th'로 만든다.
④ 나이나 개수 등을 말할 때는 기수를 사용한다.
⑤ 100 이상의 숫자는 서수로 만들 수 없다.

02 다음 중 성격이 <u>다른</u> 것은?

02
서수와 기수를 구분한다

① second   ② sixteen
③ fifth   ④ eighth
⑤ eleventh

03 다음 숫자를 기수와 서수로 쓰시오.

```
      ┌ 기수 _____
  8  ─┤
      └ 서수 _____
```

O4 다음 서수를 표기한 것 중 <u>잘못된</u> 것은?

① 3rd - third
② 1st - first
③ 4th - forth
④ 13th - thirteenth
⑤ 10th - tenth

O5 다음 문장 중 바르지 <u>않은</u> 것은?

① I have three books.
② My sister is in two grade.
③ There are five bananas on the table.
④ Paul is her first child.
⑤ You pay ten dollars for this shirt.

O6 다음은 기수를 서수로 고친 것이다. <u>틀린</u> 부분을 바르게 고쳐 쓰시오.

| 21 → twentieth - first |

_____ ⇨ _____

O7 다음을 바르게 읽은 것은?

> 20.13 meters

① twenty point one three meters
② two oh point thirteen meters
③ twentieth point thirteen meters
④ twenty point thirteen meters
⑤ two oh one three meters

O8 다음 분수를 바르게 읽은 것은?

> $\dfrac{3}{7}$

① three-seventh
② third-seven
③ three-sevenths
④ third-sevenths
⑤ three-seven

09 다음 전화번호를 영어로 읽을 때, 틀린 부분을 바르게 고쳐 쓰시오.

> 031-345-xxxx :
>
> oh three one, three four five xxxx

_____ ⇨ _____

10 다음 질문에 대한 답이 1998년이라고 할 때, 가장 바르게 말한 것은?

> A : What year was it?
>
> B : (1998).

① It was a thousand nine hundred ninety eight.
② It was nineteen ninety-eight.
③ It was nineteen nine eight.
④ It was one nine ninety-eight.
⑤ It was one nine nine eight.

Quiz!

다음 ( ) 안의 숫자를 기수 또는 서수로 알맞게 고쳐 써 보자.

1 _____ month of the year is January. (1)

2 I have _____ cats. (3)

3 My office is on _____ floor. (4)

4 The hotel has _____ bedrooms. (50)

5 Your school is behind _____ building. (9)

6 This is _____ meeting. (2)

7 She makes _____ questions. (15)

다음 숫자들을 영어로 읽어 보자.

1 1958년

_____ fifty eight

2 $14.61

fourteen _____ _____ cents

3 02-413-xxxx

_____ two, _____ _____ three, xxxx

4 47.15

_____ _____ one five

5 1961년 7월 5일 금요일

_____, _____ five, nineteen sixty one

6 $\dfrac{3}{5}$ three _____

Unit 0**2**

비인칭 주어

비인칭주어 it은 시간, 날씨, 거리, 날짜,
명암, 요일 등을 나타낼 때 쓰인다.
비인칭주어 it은 따로 해석하지 않는다.

비인칭주어

비인칭주어란?

시간, 날씨, 거리, 명암, 요일, 날짜 등을 나타내는 문장에서 주어로 쓰이는 it을 말한다. 이때 it은 특별한 뜻을 갖지 않으므로, 별도의 해석을 하지 않는다.

1 비인칭 주어의 활용

1 날씨

How's the weather? 날씨가 어때?

= What's the weather **like**?

– **It** is cold today. 오늘은 추워.

2 요일

What day is it? 무슨 요일이니?   – **It** is Monday today. 오늘은 월요일이야.

3 날짜

What date is it? 며칠이니?

= What's the **date**?   – **It**'s May 15. 5월 15일이야.

> **Tip!**
> 비인칭주어를 사용하는 그 밖의 경우
> What month is it? (월) 몇 월이니?
> What season is it? (계절) 무슨 계절이니?
> What year is it? (연도) 몇 년도이니?
> It is 80 miles from here to the post office. (거리)
> 여기부터 우체국까지 거리는 80마일이다.
> It's dark here. (명암) 여기는 어둡다.

4 시간

What time is it? 몇 시니?

= What's the time?

= What time do you have?

= Do you have the time?   – **It** is 8 o'clock. 8시 정각이야.

　　cf. Do you have time? 시간 있니?   – Yes, I do. 응, 있어

2 시간 말하기

1 □시 □분의 순서로 말하기

시에 해당하는 숫자와 분에 해당하는 숫자를 기수로 말한다.

ex. 9시 03분 : nine oh three　　　　9시 10분 : nine ten
　　　　　　　　시　　　분　　　　　　　　　　시　　분
　　　　　*oh는 '~분'이 한 자리 숫자일 때 혼동하지 않도록 넣어 준다.

② □분 □시의 순서로 말하기

past(after), to를 이용하여 말한다.

> **Tip!**
> 'past/after~'는 '~가 지나서'를 뜻하고 'to~'는 '~를 향해서, ~전에'를 뜻하다.
> to대신 before를 써도 되나 보통 간단하게 말하는 것을 선호하므로 before는 잘 사용하지 않는다.

3시(지난) 5분

five	past / after	three
분		시

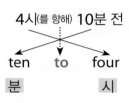

4시(를 향해) 10분 전

ten	to	four
분		시

③ 15분, 30분, 45분 말하기

▶ 15분, 30분, 45분은 □시 + □분의 순서로 나타내기도 하지만, a quarter, half past, after, to를 사용해서 □분 + □시의 순으로 나타내기도 한다.

> **Tip!**
> • a quarter = 15분
> (60분의 1/4을 나타내므로 15분)
> half = 30분, 반
> (60분의 1/2를 나타내므로 30분)
> • past, after, to를 이용하여 15분, 30분을 나타낼 경우 fifteen이나 thirty보다는 a quarter, half를 사용한다.
> *ex.* a quarter past nine
> ~~fifteen past nine~~
> half past nine
> ~~thirty past nine~~

9시(를 향해) 15분 전(8시 45분)

a quarter **to** nine

7시(지난) 반 (7시 30분)

✗half   past   seven

half 앞에서는 a를 붙이지 않는다.

▶ a quarter은 past(after), to와 함께 올 수 있으나 half는 past만 사용한다.

a quarter **to** □시

a quarter **past** □시
after

half **past** □시

다음 대화의 빈칸에 알맞은 말을 써 보자.

January 1월
Monday 월요일
March 3월
cloudy 흐린
windy 바람 부는
August 8월

1 *What* *month* is it?
– It's January.

2 _____ _____ is it?
– It's Monday.

3 _____ you have _____ time?
= What _____ do you have?
– It's ten twelve.

4 What's the _____ today?
– _____ is March 3rd.

5 _____ _____ is it?
– It's twenty past ten.

6 What _____ is it?
– _____ is winter.

7 _____ _____ is it?
– _____ is 2005.

8 _____ the weather?
– It's cloudy and windy.

9 What's the weather _____ ?
– _____ is rainy.

10 _____ _____ the date today?
– It's August 10, 2009.

2

다음 대화의 빈칸에 알맞은 말을 써 보자.

1 Do you   *have*   the time?

– ___*It*___ is 4 o'clock.

2 What _____ is it?

– It is April.

3 What's the _____ today?

– It is January 10, 1989.

4 What's the _____ _____ ?

– _____ is hot and sunny.

5 What _____ is it today?

– It is Thursday.

6 What _____ is it?

– It is half past two.

7 Do you have _____ ?

– No, I don't. I'm busy.

8 How's the _____ in Paris?

– _____ is foggy.

9 What time _____ you _____ ?

= What time _____ _____ ?

– It is twelve to eleven.

10 What _____ is it?

– _____ is summer.

Thursday 목요일
busy 바쁜
foggy 안개 낀

다음 빈칸을 숫자로 채우고, ( ) 안에서 알맞은 말을 골라 보자.

midnight 자정
a quarter 4분의1 (15분)

1 It's three to two.

　2　시　　3　(분, 분 전)입니다.

2 It's seven oh four.

　　시　　　(분, 분 전)입니다.

3 It's midnight.

(자정, 정오)　　시입니다.

4 It's a quarter past five.

　　시　　　(분, 분 전)입니다.

5 It's three forty.

　　시　　　(분, 분 전)입니다.

6 It's a quarter to one.

　　시　　　(분, 분 전)입니다.

7 It's twenty-five after eleven.

　　시　　　(분, 분 전)입니다.

8 It's ten fifteen.

　　시　　　(분, 분 전)입니다.

9 It's half past four.

　　시　　　(분, 분 전)입니다.

10 It's seven to six.

　　시　　　(분, 분 전)입니다.

4

다음 빈칸을 숫자로 채우고, (   ) 안에서 알맞은 말을 골라 보자.

1 It's fourteen after three.

   3 시   *14* ((분), 분 전)입니다.

2 It's eleven fifteen.

   □ 시   □ (분, 분 전)입니다.

3 It's twelve oh six.

   □ 시   □ (분, 분 전)입니다.

4 It's a quarter past seven.

   □ 시   □ (분, 분 전)입니다.

5 It's seven twenty.

   □ 시   □ (분, 분 전)입니다.

6 It's half past nine.

   □ 시   □ (분, 분 전)입니다.

7 It's a quarter to twelve.

   □ 시   □ (분, 분 전)입니다.

8 It's thirty-two past seven.

   □ 시   □ (분, 분 전)입니다.

9 It's eight to eleven.

   □ 시   □ (분, 분 전)입니다.

10 It's eighteen after five.

   □ 시   □ (분, 분 전)입니다.

다음 대답에 알맞은 질문을 완성해 보자.

1 What _day_ _is_ _it_ ?

– It is Friday.

2 What _____ _____ _____ ?

– It's June 14, 2005.

3 What _____ _____ _____ ?

– It's 2009.

4 _____ the weather like?

– It is sunny.

5 What's _____ _____ ?

– It's half past three.

6 What _____ _____ _____ ?

– It is May.

7 How's _____ _____ ?

– It is cold today.

8 Do you _____ _____ _____ ?

– It's a quarter to ten.

9 What _____ _____ _____ ?

– It's spring.

10 What time _____ _____ _____ _____ ?

– It's ten thirty.

2

다음 대답에 알맞은 질문을 완성해 보자.

1 What   *time*   *is*   *it*   ?
– It's ten to three.

2 How's ____ ____ ?
– It's cloudy.

3 What ____ ____ ____ ?
– It's Wednesday.

4 What ____ ____ ____ ?
– It's winter.

5 What's the weather ____ ?
– It's rainy.

6 What ____ ____ ____ ?
– It's the 2nd of October.

7 What ____ ____ ____ ?
– It's Monday.

8 Do you ____ ____ ?
– Yes, I do.

9 What's ____ ____ today?
– It's November 4, 2010.

10 What ____ ____ ____ ?
– It's 1988.

October 10월
November 11월

다음 시각을 영어로 써 보자.

1

seven ___twenty five___

___twenty five___ past ___seven___

2

_____ fifty

_____ _____ one

3

_____ _____

4

twelve _____

twenty _____ _____

5

_____ _____ five

6

_____ fifteen

_____ after five

4

다음 시각을 영어로 써 보자.

1

___*three*___ ___*o'clock*___

2

four _____ five

_____ after _____

3

_____ _____ six

4

twelve _____

twenty five _____ _____

5

ten _____ one

ten _____ one

6

_____ _____ three

다음 밑줄 친 부분들 중에서 틀린 곳을 바르게 고쳐 써 보자.

1 What's the <u>weather</u>?　　　– <u>It's</u> cloudy.
　　weather like

2 <u>What</u> <u>month</u> is it?　　　– It's 2011.

3 What <u>date</u> is it today?　　　– <u>It's</u> Monday.

4 Do you have <u>the time</u>?　　　– Yes, I <u>do</u>.

5 What <u>year</u> is it?　　　– <u>This</u> is 2015.

6 <u>What</u> <u>day</u> is it?　　　– It's winter.

7 <u>That's</u> bright <u>here</u>.

8 It's <u>quarter</u> <u>to</u> four. (4시 15분전)

9 <u>How</u> <u>month</u> is it?　　　– It's December.

10 How's the weather <u>like</u>?　　　– It's <u>windy</u>.

11 What's the <u>weather</u> today?　　　– It's <u>cold</u> today.

12 What's the <u>day</u> today?　　　– August <u>27</u>.

13 <u>How</u> year is it?　　　– <u>2000</u>.

14 What <u>month</u> is <u>it</u>?　　　– It's fall.

15 What <u>date</u> is it?　　　– It's <u>the five</u> of December.

다음 밑줄 친 부분들 중에서 틀린 곳을 바르게 고쳐 써 보자.

1 What <u>time</u> is it now? – <u>Fifteen</u> past three.
                                   A quarter

2 Do you have <u>time</u>? – It's three <u>forty</u>.

3 <u>It's</u> five <u>past</u> three. (3시 5분 전입니다.)

4 <u>It's</u> twenty five <u>to</u> seven. (7시 25분입니다.)

5 It's <u>a half</u> <u>past</u> ten. (10시 반입니다.)

6 <u>That's</u> <u>midnight</u>. (자정입니다.)

7 <u>What</u> time do you have? – It's half <u>after</u> seven.

8 What's <u>the time</u>? – It's <u>to two a quarter</u>. (2시 15분전입니다.)

9 It's <u>thirteen</u> <u>after</u> five. (5시 13분 전입니다.)

10 <u>What's</u> the time? – It's half <u>to</u> four. (4시 30분입니다.)

11 What time is <u>that</u>? – It's <u>half</u> past seven.

12 Do you have <u>time</u>? – No, <u>it's not</u>.

13 What's the <u>time</u>? – It's <u>sixteen twelve</u>. (12시 16분입니다.)

14 It's <u>quarter</u> <u>past</u> five. (5시 15분입니다.)

15 It's <u>half</u> <u>to</u> eight. (8시 반입니다.)

01 다음 빈칸에 공통으로 들어갈 말로 알맞은 것은?

> · _____ is 3 o'clock.
>
> · _____ is February 2nd.

① This   ② That
③ It   ④ She
⑤ I

02 다음 빈칸에 알맞은 말을 쓰시오.

> How's the weather?
>
> = What's the weather _____ ?

03 다음 주어진 시각을 영어로 나타낼 때, 빈칸에 알맞은 말을 쓰시오.

> 2시 13분 : _____ thirteen
>
>   thirteen _____ two
>
>   thirteen _____ two

04 다음 주어진 시각을 영어로 나타낼 때, 빈칸에 들어갈 말이 순서대로 바르게 짝지어진 것은?

> 6시 50분 : six _____
>
>   ten to _____

① fifteen - six   ② fifteen - seven
③ fifteen - five   ④ fifty - seven
⑤ ten - six

05 다음 주어진 시각을 영어로 나타낸 것 중 <u>잘못된</u> 것은? (2개)

> 4시 15분

① Four fifteen.
② A quarter past four.
③ A quarter after four.
④ Fifteen past four.
⑤ Fifteen after four.

06 다음 중 밑줄 친 부분의 용법이 <u>다른</u> 것은?

① <u>It</u>'s dark here.
② <u>It</u>'s a piano.
③ <u>It</u>'s summer.
④ <u>It</u>'s June 30th.
⑤ <u>It</u>'s 8 o'clock.

실전Test

07 다음 빈칸에 들어갈 질문으로 알맞은 것은?

> A : _____
>
> B : Sunday.

① What date is it?
② What day is it?
③ What month is it?
④ What year is it?
⑤ What time is it?

08 다음 대화의 빈칸에 들어갈 말로 알맞은 것은?

> A : What's the _____ today?
>
> B : It's March 16th.

① time   ② day
③ month   ④ year
⑤ date

더 알아보기

07
요일로 답하고 있으므로
요일을 묻는 의문문이
필요하다.

08
날짜로 답하고 있다.

09 다음 밑줄 친 부분의 우리말 뜻으로 바른 것은?

> What time is it?
> – It's <u>two to one</u>.

① 2시 1분
② 1시 2분
③ 1시 2분 전
④ 2시 1분 전
⑤ 12시쯤

10 다음 질문에 대한 알맞은 대답을 |보기|에서 고르시오.

> |보기| ⓐ It's three ten.   ⓑ Yes, I do.

(A) Do you have the time?   –

(B) Do you have time?   – _____

Quiz!

다음 대답에 알맞은 질문을 써 보자.

1 A : _____ _____ is it?

B : It's May 15.

2 A : What's the weather _____ ?

B : It's rainy.

3 A : _____ _____ is it?

B : It's Saturday.

4 A : _____ _____ is it?

B : It's summer.

5 A : _____ _____ is it?

B : It's 2010.

다음 우리말을 영어로 써 보자.

1 6시 30분   six _____

   _____ _____ six

2 8시 26분   _____ twenty-six

   twenty-six _____ _____

3 10시 15분 전   a quarter _____ _____

4 4시 8분 전   _____ _____ four

5 3시 15분   three _____

   _____ _____ three

   _____ _____ three

Unit o**3**

be동사, 일반동사 과거형의 긍정문

be동사의 과거형은 was, were가 있으며,
일반동사의 과거형은 규칙 변화를 하는 것과
불규칙 변화를 하는 것이 있다.

be동사, 일반동사 과거형의 긍정문

동사의 과거형이란?

과거에 일어난 일을 나타낼 때 사용되는 동사의 형태를 말한다.

1 be동사 과거형의 긍정문

be동사의 현재형(am, are, is)을 과거형(was, were)으로 바꿔 주면 된다.

ex. I **was** healthy.   나는 건강했다.

You **were** healthy.   너는 건강했다.

He **was** healthy.   그는 건강했다.

She **was** healthy.   그녀는 건강했다.

We **were** healthy.   우리는 건강했다.

You **were** healthy.   너희들은 건강했다.

they **were** healthy.   그들은 건강했다.

단수		복수	
I	was~.	We	
You	were~.	You	were~.
He, She, It, Tom	was~.	They	

일반동사 과거형의 긍정문

일반동사의 현재형을 과거형으로 바꿔 주면 된다. 일반동사의 과거형은 주어의 수와 인칭의 영향을 받지 않는다. 즉, 주어가 3인칭 단수이어도 s/es가 붙지 않는다.

ex. I **went** to school at 8.　　　나는 8시에 학교에 갔다.

　　He **went** to school at 8.　　그는 8시에 학교에 갔다.

단수		복수	
I		We	
You	work**ed**.	You	work**ed**.
He, She, It, Tom		They	

일반동사의 과거형에는 규칙적인 변화를 하는 것과 불규칙적인 변화를 하는 것 두 종류가 있다.

1 규칙 변화 동사의 과거형

규칙 변화 동사의 과거형은 동사 끝부분에 **ed**를 붙여 만든다.

동사	공식	예
대부분의 동사	+ ed	work → work**ed**
e로 끝나는 동사	+ d	like → lik**ed** smile → smil**ed**
「자음＋y」로 끝나는 동사	y → ied	carry → carr**ied** study → stud**ied**
「단모음 + 단자음」으로 끝나는 동사	마지막 자음 하나 더 붙이고 + ed	rub → rub**bed** stop → stop**ped** drop → drop**ped** permit → permit**ted**
「단모음 + 단자음」으로 끝나지만, 앞 음절에 강세가 오는 경우	+ ed	lísten → listen**ed** ópen → open**ed** vísit → visit**ed**

smile 미소짓다
carry 운반하다
rub 문지르다
drop 떨어뜨리다
permit 허락하다
listen 듣다
visit 방문하다

2 불규칙 변화 동사의 과거형

불규칙 변화 동사는 과거형을 만들기 위한 특별한 방법이 없다. 따라서 변화 형태를 암기해 야만 한다.

큰 소리로 열 번 읽어 보자. 책을 보고 ○○○○○ ○○○○○
                                      책을 덮고 ○○○○○ ○○○○○

현재 – 과거	현재 – 과거
do 하다 → did	tell 말하다 → told
go 가다 → went	find 발견하다 → found
see 보다 → saw	hear 듣다 → heard
eat 먹다 → ate	stand 서다 → stood
wear 입다 → wore	understand 이해하다 → understood
drink 마시다 → drank	meet 만나다 → met
win 이기다 → won	get 얻다 → got
begin 시작하다 → began	sleep 잠자다 → slept
swim 수영하다 → swam	leave 떠나다 → left
draw 그리다 → drew	keep 기르다, 유지하다 → kept
give 주다 → gave	send 보내다 → sent
take 잡다, 타다 → took	spend 소비하다 → spent
drive 운전하다 → drove	feel 느끼다 → felt
write 쓰다 → wrote	sit 앉다 → sat
fall 떨어지다 → fell	lose 잃다, 지다 → lost
break 부수다 → broke	teach 가르치다 → taught
speak 말하다 → spoke	buy 사다 → bought
choose 선택하다 → chose	catch 잡다 → caught
run 달리다 → ran	think 생각하다 → thought
come 오다 → came	cut 자르다 → cut
have 가지다 → had	hit 치다 → hit
make 만들다 → made	put 놓다, 두다 → put
say 말하다 → said	read 읽다 → read
sell 팔다 → sold	cost 비용이 들다 → cost

다음 문장에서 동사에 동그라미 하고 시제를 고른 후, 우리말 뜻을 써 보자.

1 I ⓐam ill now. (**현재**, 과거)
나는 지금 _아프다_ .
I was ill at that time. (현재, **과거**)
나는 그 당시에 .

2 He was a lawyer. (현재, 과거)
그는 변호사 .
He is a lawyer. (현재, 과거)
그는 변호사 .

3 He worked harder. (현재, 과거)
그는 더 열심히 .
He works harder. (현재, 과거)
그는 더 열심히 .

4 The boy puts on the black cap. (현재, 과거)
그 소년은 검정색 모자를 .
The boy put on the black cap. (현재, 과거)
그 소년은 검정색 모자를 .

5 Jane sent a text message. (현재, 과거)
Jane은 문자메시지를 .
Jane sends a text message. (현재, 과거)
Jane은 문자메시지를 .

lawyer 변호사
put on 입다, 쓰다
text message 문자메시지

4 put은 현재형과 과거형이
같다. 주어가 3인칭 단수
일때 현재형에만 s가
붙는다.

다음 ( ) 안에서 알맞은 말을 골라 동그라미 해 보자.

kind-hearted 마음씨가
좋은
barber 이발사
be on vacation 휴가 중이다
bear 곰
dead 죽은
favorite 가장 좋아하는
present 선물

4 무생물의 소유격은 s를
붙여서 만들지 않고 of를
이용하여 소유격을
만든다.

ex. the color of the house
그 집의 색깔

1 Judy (was, were) kind-hearted.

2 You (was, were) a barber.

3 Mr. Kim (was, were) on vacation.

4 The color of the house (was, were) yellow.

5 She and I (was, were) classmates.

6 My friends (was, were) hungry.

7 The students (was, were) good.

8 There (was, were) an elephant in the field.

9 Minho and Tom (was, were) kind.

10 The bears (was, were) dead.

11 The building (was, were) very clean.

12 My favorite food (was, were) cheese pizza.

13 The presents (was, were) some books.

14 He (was, were) rich.

15 We (was, were) in the video store.

3

다음 빈칸에 동사의 과거형을 써 보자.

1	end	*ended*	**2**	work	
3	live		**4**	marry	
5	study		**6**	look	
7	play		**8**	wash	
9	enjoy		**10**	pull	
11	visit		**12**	listen	
13	like		**14**	wax	
15	rain		**16**	worry	
17	dry		**18**	drop	
19	smile		**20**	love	
21	stop		**22**	walk	
23	open		**24**	snow	
25	rub		**26**	pray	
27	try		**28**	turn	
29	carry		**30**	fix	

rub 문지르다
wax 왁스칠을 하다
worry 걱정하다
drop 떨어뜨리다

다음 빈칸에 동사의 과거형을 써 보자.

1	be	*was, were*	2	speak	
3	do		4	run	
5	go		6	come	
7	see		8	have	
9	drink		10	make	
11	begin		12	say	
13	swim		14	sell	
15	draw		16	tell	
17	eat		18	find	
19	give		20	meet	
21	take		22	get	
23	drive		24	sleep	
25	write		26	leave	
27	fall		28	keep	
29	break		30	send	

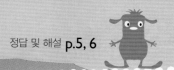

5

다음 빈칸에 동사의 과거형을 써 보자.

1 spend — *spent*

2 run

3 feel

4 speak

5 sit

6 have

7 lose

8 see

9 win

10 wake

11 hear

12 be

13 stand

14 take

15 understand

16 make

17 do

18 swim

19 buy

20 teach

21 catch

22 write

23 think

24 leave

25 cut

26 fall

27 put

28 meet

29 read

30 give

다음 빈칸에 동사의 과거형을 써 보자.

1 send	*sent*	2 drive	
3 get		4 say	
5 do		6 find	
7 tell		8 cut	
9 drink		10 go	
11 keep		12 lose	
13 come		14 hear	
15 buy		16 spend	
17 sit		18 catch	
19 teach		20 break	
21 sleep		22 take	
23 think		24 eat	
25 understand		26 fall	
27 put		28 sell	
29 begin		30 draw	

7

(   ) 안에 주어진 동사를 우리말에 알맞게 바꿔 보자.

1 I | *am* | tired. (be) 나는 피곤하다.

  I | | tired. 나는 피곤했다.

2 You | | very kind-hearted. (be) 너는 매우 친절했다.

  You | | very kind-hearted. 너는 매우 친절하다.

3 She | | a beautiful scarf. (wear)

  그녀는 아름다운 스카프를 했다.

  She | | a beautiful scarf.

  그녀는 아름다운 스카프를 한다.

4 She | | sun block lotion. (wear)

  그녀는 자외선 차단 로션을 바른다.

  She | | sun block lotion.

  그녀는 자외선 차단 로션을 발랐다.

5 Bill | | a newspaper. (read)

  Bill은 신문을 읽었다.

  Bill | | a newspaper.

  Bill은 신문을 읽는다.

6 A dog | | at a cat. (bark) 한 마리 개가 고양이를 보고 짖었다.

  A dog | | at a cat. 한 마리 개가 고양이를 보고 짖는다.

7 Jane | | to play tennis with him. (ask)

  Jane은 그에게 테니스를 치자고 부탁한다.

  Jane | | to play tennis with him.

  Jane은 그에게 테니스를 치자고 부탁했다.

wear 입다/바르다
sun block lotion 자외선
차단 로션
newspaper 신문

다음 주어진 문장을 과거형으로 바꿔 보자.

good–looking 잘생긴
postman 우편배달부
brave 용감한

1 I am a scientist.

⇨ I ___was___ a scientist.

2 The dog is very smart.

⇨ The dog _____ very smart.

3 We are farmers.

⇨ We _____ farmers.

4 Tom is good-looking.

⇨ Tom _____ good-looking.

5 You are an actor.

⇨ You _____ an actor.

6 They are taxi drivers.

⇨ They _____ taxi drivers.

7 The game is exciting.

⇨ The game _____ exciting.

8 He is a postman.

⇨ He _____ a postman.

9 Mr. Kim and his wife are rich lawyers.

⇨ Mr. Kim and his wife _____ rich lawyers.

10 The young man is very brave.

⇨ The young man _____ very brave.

2

다음 주어진 문장을 과거형으로 바꿔 보자.

1 I walk to church.

⇨ I 　*walked*　 to church.

2 He drinks a cup of coffee.

⇨ He 　　　　　 a cup of coffee.

3 We like him a lot.

⇨ We 　　　　　 him a lot.

4 She sits on the bench.

⇨ She 　　　　　 on the bench.

5 Tom hears her voice.

⇨ Tom 　　　　　 her voice.

6 Your sister runs into the market.

⇨ Your sister 　　　　　 into the market.

7 Jane takes a taxi.

⇨ Jane 　　　　　 a taxi.

8 The train starts at 10 every day.

⇨ The train 　　　　　 at 10 every day.

9 I drive the truck.

⇨ I 　　　　　 the truck.

10 Jane reads the novel.

⇨ Jane 　　　　　 the novel.

a lot 많이
novel 소설

주어진 문장의 시제를 고르고 우리말에 맞게 동사의 알맞은 형태를 빈칸에 써 보자.

early bird 부지런한 새
worm 벌레
allowance 용돈
test paper 시험지
take a rest 시험을 치다

1 The early bird   *catches*   the worm. (catch)   (현재, 과거)
일찍 일어나는 새가 벌레를 잡는다.

2 He _____ his wallet a few minutes ago. (lose)   (현재, 과거)
그는 몇 분 전에 그의 지갑을 잃어 버렸다.

3 The rain _____ then. (stop)   (현재, 과거)
그 때 비가 그쳤다.

4 We _____ a lot of snow in December. (have)   (현재, 과거)
12월에 눈이 많이 온다.

5 Jim _____ all of his allowance yesterday. (spend)   (현재, 과거)
Jim은 어제 그의 용돈 전부를 썼다.

6 Spring _____ after winter. (come)   (현재, 과거)
겨울 뒤에 봄이 온다.

7 My teacher _____ the test paper to me. (give)   (현재, 과거)
나의 선생님은 나에게 시험지를 주셨다.

8 The sun _____ in the west. (set)   (현재, 과거)
해는 서쪽에서 진다.

9 He _____ a test this morning. (take)   (현재, 과거)
그는 오늘 아침 시험을 쳤다.

10 Ann _____ to her sister. (talk)   (현재, 과거)
Ann은 그녀의 여동생에게 말했다.

4

주어진 문장의 시제를 고르고 우리말에 맞게 동사의 알맞은 형태를 빈칸에 써 보자.

1 She ___got___ a good grade last year.(get)　　　(현재, 과거)
그녀는 작년에 좋은 성적을 받았다.

2 Water _____ at 100℃.(boil)　　　(현재, 과거)
물은 100℃에서 끓는다.

3 Tom _____ the ticket in his pocket.(put)　　　(현재, 과거)
Tom은 그 표를 그의 호주머니에 넣었다.

4 Jane _____ pain now.(feel)　　　(현재, 과거)
그녀는 지금 통증을 느낀다.

5 I _____ to a train one hour ago.(transfer)　　　(현재, 과거)
나는 한 시간 전에 기차를 갈아탔다.

6 Mary always _____ hello to me.(say)　　　(현재, 과거)
Mary는 항상 나에게 인사한다.

7 Some ice cream _____ on his pants.(fall)　　　(현재, 과거)
약간의 아이스크림이 그의 바지에 떨어졌다.

8 He _____ yesterday.(shave)　　　(현재, 과거)
그는 어제 면도했다.

9 This sofa _____ handmade.(be)　　　(현재, 과거)
이 소파는 수작업 한 것이다.

10 The earth _____ around the sun.(move)　　　(현재, 과거)
지구는 태양 주위를 돈다.

boil 끓다
put 넣다
transfer 옮기다, 이동하다
shave 면도하다
move 움직이다

다음 밑줄 친 부분들 중에서 <u>틀린</u> 곳을 바르게 고쳐 써 보자.

last week 지난 주
fall down 떨어지다
ground 땅
megazine 잡지
stormy 폭풍(우)의
receive 받다
businessman 사업가
last night 어젯 밤
then 그때
the day before yesterday
그저께
two years ago 2년 전에
two hours ago 2시간 전에

1 Judy <u>were</u> <u>busy</u> yesterday.
　　　　was

2 <u>She</u> <u>draws</u> her mother last week.

3 He <u>falled</u> <u>down</u> on the ground last night.

4 Minsu and she <u>was</u> very <u>angry</u> then.

5 <u>My father</u> <u>reads</u> a magazine yesterday.

6 We <u>was</u> <u>in</u> our classroom then.

7 Mr. Brown <u>cutted</u> the cake <u>with</u> his wife last night.

8 He <u>draws</u> a picture to his son the day <u>before</u> yesterday.

9 It <u>is</u> very <u>stormy</u> the day before yesterday.

10 I <u>receive</u> a lot of <u>letters</u> two years ago.

11 John <u>wents</u> <u>camping</u> with Paul last summer.

12 My cousin <u>begins</u> his <u>work</u> last year.

13 She <u>speaked</u> <u>to</u> her students yesterday.

14 <u>The businessmen</u> was very <u>busy</u>.

15 Your brother <u>do</u> his homework two <u>hours</u> ago.

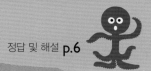

다음 밑줄 친 부분들 중에서 틀린 곳을 바르게 고쳐 써 보자.

1 He <u>dryed</u> his <u>hair</u> 30 minutes ago.
　　 dried

2 Subin and Minsu <u>was</u> <u>always</u> happy at that time.

3 <u>We</u> <u>win</u> the soccer game last month.

4 <u>She</u> <u>text</u> just now.

5 He <u>hitted</u> a dog with <u>his cane</u> yesterday.

6 Sumi <u>were</u> <u>free</u> last week.

7 <u>The man</u> <u>buys</u> a black helmet yesterday.

8 She <u>looks</u> after <u>a lot of</u> children last year.

9 My son <u>droped</u> his glasses <u>then</u>.

10 I <u>come</u> back to his office 10 minutes <u>ago</u>.

11 The <u>women</u> was <u>beautiful</u>.

12 <u>The baby</u> <u>sleeps</u> well last night.

13 He <u>getted</u> some food <u>from</u> her yesterday.

14 <u>My mother</u> <u>breaked</u> the dish a few minutes ago.

15 They <u>was</u> very <u>cute</u> then.

text 문자를 보내다
cane 지팡이
helmet 헬멧
drop 떨어뜨리다
break 깨뜨리다
mice mouse(쥐)의 복수형
30 minutes ago 30분 전에
10 minutes ago 10분 전에
a few minutes ago 몇 분
전에
at that time 그 때에
just now 방금 전에

[01–02] 다음 중 동사의 과거형이 바르게 연결되지 <u>않은</u> 것을 고르시오.

01
① begin - began
② take - took
③ try - tried
④ stop - stopped
⑤ spend- spended

02
① buy - bought
② tell - told
③ hear - heared
④ sell - sold
⑤ think - thought

[03–04] 다음 문장 중 올바른 것을 고르시오.

03
① My sister stoped swimming.
② She climbbed the mountain.
③ The students openned their books.
④ It snowed a lot last year.
⑤ He droped his glasses.

04
① I carryed her bag to the hotel.
② The wolf catched a little bird.
③ The boy swam very well.
④ Judy visitted Tom.
⑤ He haved a good time.

05 다음 빈칸에 들어갈 말이 순서대로 바르게 짝지어진 것은?

> • I _____ a good skater.
>
> • Jane and Adam _____ my English teachers now.
>
> • The house _____ very beautiful last year.

① am - is - was   ② was - is - were
③ were - are - were   ④ am - are - was
⑤ am - are - were

06 다음 빈칸에 들어갈 말로 알맞은 것은?

> I lost my bag _____.

① now
② tomorrow
③ tomorrow morning
④ last month
⑤ next week

07 다음 문장에서 <u>틀린</u> 것을 바르게 고쳐 쓰시오.

> She and I was classmates last year.

_____ ⇨ _____

07
주어는 She and I
이며, 복수이다.

08 다음 문장을 과거형으로 바꿀 때, 올바른 것은?

> My father puts his hat on the table.

① My father is putting his hat on the table.
② My father putted his hat on the table.
③ My father is put his hat on the table.
④ My father put his hat on the table.
⑤ My father is putted his hat on the table.

09 다음 문장의 시제에 맞도록 ( ) 안의 동사를 바르게 바꿔 쓰시오.

(1) Minsu _____ TV last night. (watch)

(2) He _____ a cell phone last week. (buy)

(3) We _____ in the library yesterday evening. (be)

10 다음 빈칸에 들어갈 말로 알맞지 <u>않은</u> 것은?

Jenny _____.

① hates carrots
② always speaks English
③ looked at the picture on the wall
④ worked last night
⑤ dances with Jinho the day before yesterday

09

the day before
yesterday 그저께

1, 3인칭 단수의
be동사의 과거형은
was이고, 주어가
복수인 경우 be동사의
과거형은 were이다.
문장 끝의 때를
나타내는 부사와
동사의 시제를
일치시켜야 한다.

정답 및 해설 p.6, 7

주어진 동사를 우리말에 알맞게 바꿔 보자.

1 His sisters _____ very beautiful. (be)

그의 여동생들은 매우 아름답다.

2 The boys _____ yesterday morning. (leave)

그 소년들은 어제 아침 떠났다.

3 I _____ to the market with my brother. (walk)

나는 나의 동생과 시장에 걸어간다.

4 The clerk _____ a lot of sneakers. (sell) clerk 점원   sneaker 운동화

그 점원은 많은 운동화를 팔았다.

5 Mary _____ her earings under the sofa. (put)

Mary는 그녀의 귀걸이를 소파 아래에 둔다.

6 The lion _____ a deer. (catch)

그 사자는 사슴 한 마리를 잡았다.

7 She _____ taking pictures. (stop)

그녀는 사진촬영을 멈추었다.

8 Tom _____ very glad. (be)

Tom은 매우 기뻤다.

9 The kid _____ to cry. (begin)

그 아이는 울기 시작했다.

10 He _____ her some chocolate. (give)

그는 그녀에게 약간의 초콜릿을 주었다.

Unit **04**

과거형의 부정문, 의문문

be동사 과거형의 부정문과 의문문에는
was/were, wasn't/weren't를 쓰며,
일반동사 과거형의 부정문과 의문문에는
did, didn't 를 쓴다.

과거형의 부정문, 의문문

① be동사 과거형의 부정문, 의문문

① 부정문

현재형의 부정문과 마찬가지로 be동사의 과거형 was, were 바로 뒤에 **not**만 붙이면 된다.

ex. I **wasn't** at school then.
나는 그 때 학교에 있지 않았다.
We **weren't** at school then.
우리는 그 때 학교에 있지 않았다.

단수			복수		
I	wasn't		We		
You	weren't	~.	You	weren't	~.
He/She/It/ Tom	wasn't		They		

* was not의 축약형은 wasn't, were not의 축약형은 weren't이다.

② 의문문

현재형의 의문문과 마찬가지로 be동사의 과거형 was, were가 주어 앞으로 오면 된다.
Yes, No로 대답하고 was/were로 질문했으므로 was/were로 받는다.

ex. **Were** you a student then? 너는 그때 학생이었니?

　　– Yes, I **was.**　　네. 그랬어요.
　　– No, I **wasn't.**　　아니요, 그렇지 않았어요.

단수			복수		
Was	I			we	
Were	you	~?	Were	you	~?
Was	he, she, it, Tom			they	

2 일반동사 과거형의 부정문, 의문문

1 부정문

don't나 doesn't 대신 수와 인칭에 관계없이
didn't를 사용하고 뒤에는 동사원형이 온다.

ex. I **didn't** go to school.
나는 학교에 가지 않았다.

He **didn't** go to school.
그는 학교에 가지 않았다.

They **didn't** go to school.
그들은 학교에 가지 않았다.

단수			복수		
I			We		
You	didn't	~.	You	didn't	~.
He, She, It, Tom			They		

* did not의 축약형은 didn't이다.

2 의문문

조동사 Do, Does 대신 인칭에 상관없이 Did를 사용하고 뒤에는 동사원형이 온다.
Yes, No로 대답하고 did로 질문했으므로 did로 받는다.

ex. **Did** you go to school? 너는 학교에 갔니?

– Yes, I **did.** 네, 했어요.

– No, I **didn't.** 아니요, 하지 않았어요.

단수			복수		
Did	I	~?	Did	we	~?
	you			you	
	he, she, it, Tom			they	

다음 문장을 지시대로 바꿔 보자.

beggar 거지
carpenter 목수
friendly 친숙한, 다정한
empty 비어있는, 빈

1 The beggars were hungry.

의문문   *Were*   *the beggars*   hungry?

2 The movie was exciting.

부정문   exciting.

3 The mountain was very beautiful.

의문문   very beautiful?

4 They were lazy.

부정문   lazy.

5 There were a lot of eggs in it.

부정문   a lot of eggs in it.

6 You were carpenters.

의문문   carpenters?

7 The comic book was on the table.

부정문   on the table.

8 Joe and his cousin were friendly.

의문문   friendly?

9 The box was empty.

의문문   empty?

10 This watch was my father's.

부정문   my father's.

2

다음 질문에 Yes와 No로 시작하는 대답을 완성해 보자.

1 Were they your family?

– No, _they_ _weren't_ .

2 Was it your digital camera?

– Yes, _____ _____ .

3 Was the answer wrong?

– No, _____ _____ .

4 Were those their balls?

– No, _____ _____ .

5 Was Katherine in Canada?

– Yes, _____ _____ .

6 Was the box full with sugar?

– Yes, _____ _____ .

7 Were the games boring?

– No, _____ _____ .

8 Were Paul and Mary at the concert?

– Yes, _____ _____ .

9 Was it hand-made?

– No. _____ _____ .

10 Were the girls close friends?

– Yes, _____ _____ .

be full with ~로 가득차다
boring 지루한
close 가까운, 친한

다음을 의문문이나 부정문으로 바꿀 때, 빈칸에 알맞은 말을 써 보자.

spent spend(쓰다)의 과거형
dragonfly 잠자리
need 필요하다
attention 관심
nail shop 네일 숍
left leave의 과거
move 이사하다

1 They spent a lot of money.

의문문 _Did_ they _spend_ a lot of money?

2 Matt bought the computer game CD.

부정문 Matt _____ _____ the computer game CD.

3 I saw some tigers in the zoo.

부정문 I _____ _____ any tigers in the zoo.

4 We caught some dragonflies.

부정문 We _____ _____ any dragonflies.

5 Your brother needed your attention.

의문문 _____ your brother _____ your attention?

6 She lived in America.

의문문 _____ she _____ in America?

7 Mr. Park put his pen on the desk.

의문문 _____ Mr. Park _____ his pen on the desk?

8 Sally left the nail shop.

부정문 Sally _____ _____ the nail shop.

9 My father drove to his office?

의문문 _____ my father _____ to his office?

10 She moved to New York.

부정문 She _____ _____ to New York.

4

다음을 의문문이나 부정문으로 바꿀 때, 빈칸에 알맞은 말을 써 보자.

1 I did my best.

부정문 I _didn't_ _do_ my best.

2 He met Judy in the drugstore.

의문문 _____ he _____ Judy in the drugstore?

3 You gave me two pears.

의문문 _____ you _____ me two pears?

4 She wanted some vegetables.

부정문 She _____ _____ any vegetables.

5 They stopped jogging.

의문문 _____ they _____ jogging?

6 The students understood his explain.

부정문 The students _____ _____ his explain.

7 Tom built the church with many people.

의문문 _____ Tom _____ the church with many people?

8 My family went fishing last weekend.

의문문 _____ my family _____ fishing last weekend?

9 Jenny read the guidebook.

부정문 Jenny _____ _____ the guidebook.

10 Amy said to him, "Bye-bye."

부정문 Amy _____ _____ to him, "Bye-bye".

drugstore 약국
pear 배(과일)
vegetable 야채
guidebook 안내서

다음 문장을 지시대로 바꿔 보자.

volleyball 배구
last night 지난 밤
strange 이상한
sound 소리
how to skate 스케이트
타는 법
scribble 낙서하다

1 They played volleyball yesterday.

부정문 *They* *didn't* *play* volleyball yesterday.

2 She broke the glass last night.

의문문 　　　　　　　　　　　　 the glass last night?

3 You picked it just now.

의문문 　　　　　　　　　　　　 it just now?

4 His uncle left for France.

부정문 　　　　　　　　　　　　 for France.

5 Mary asked me some questions.

의문문 　　　　　　　　　　　　 me some questions?

6 You heard the strange sound then.

의문문 　　　　　　　　　　　 the strange sound
then?

7 He taught them history.

부정문 　　　　　　　　　　　　 them history.

8 Your daughters learned how to skate.

부정문 　　　　　　　　　　　　 how to skate.

9 You took a break time.

의문문 　　　　　　　　　　　　 a break time?

10 The girl scribbled on the wall.

부정문 　　　　　　　　　　　　 on the wall.

2

다음 질문에 Yes와 No로 시작하는 대답을 완성해 보자.

1 Did she talk about her daughter?

   – Yes,   *she*   *did*   .

2 Did he bake any bread?

   – No,   .

3 Did the students buy their school supplies?

   – No,   .

4 Did the wolf find a rabbit?

   – Yes,   .

5 Did Paul sign up yesterday?

   – Yes,   .

6 Did Anna answer the difficult question?

   – No,   .

7 Did you (너희들은) carry your textbooks?

   – Yes,   .

8 Did a cow eat a lot of grass?

   – No,   .

9 Did you(너는) make a reservation for you?

   – No,   .

10 Did you(너는) lend your brush to her?

   – Yes,   .

school supply 학교 준비물
rabbit 토끼
sign up 등록하다
text book 교과서
make a reservation
예약하다
lend 빌려주다

다음 문장의 동사에 동그라미하고 동사의 시제를 고른 후, 문장을 지시대로 바꿔 보자. 의문문은 대답도 완성해 보자.

rotten 썩은
bored 지루한
in blue 우울한
excellent 뛰어난
on vacation 휴가중

1 Your parents (are) fine. (현재), 과거)

의문문   _Are_   _your parents_   fine?   - Yes,   _they_   _are_ .

2 The woman was rich. (현재, 과거)

의문문 　　　　　　　　　　 rich?   - No, 　　　　　 .

3 My tooth is rotten. (현재, 과거)

부정문 　　　　　　　　　 rotten.

4 Your cousins were bored. (현재, 과거)

의문문 　　　　　　　　　　 bored?   - Yes, 　　　　　 .

5 The boys were exciting then. (현재, 과거)

부정문 　　　　　　　　　 exciting then.

6 James is in blue. (현재, 과거)

의문문 　　　　　　　　　　 in blue?   - Yes, 　　　　　 .

7 There were a lot of houses in this town. (현재, 과거)

의문문 　　　　　　　　　　 a lot of houses in this town?

- No, 　　　　　 .

8 The man was an excellent vet. (현재, 과거)

부정문 　　　　　　　　　 an excellent vet.

9 It was bad to me. (현재, 과거)

부정문 　　　　　　　　　 bad to me.

10 They are on vacation. (현재, 과거)

의문문 　　　　　　　　　　 on vacation?

- No, 　　　　　 .

4

다음 문장의 동사에 동그라미하고 동사의 시제를 고른 후, 문장을 지시대로
바꿔 보자. 의문문은 대답도 완성해 보자.

1 You ⟨lost⟩ the way in the forest.　　　　　　(현재, ⟨과거⟩)

　　의문문　*Did　you　lose*　the way in the forest?
　　　　　　　　　　　　　　　　　- No, *I　didn't* .

2 I introduced Jill to my parents.　　　　　　(현재, 과거)

　　부정문　　　　　　　　　　　　Jill to my parents.

3 The cap costs 30 dollars.　　　　　　　　(현재, 과거)

　　의문문　　　　　　　　　　　　30 dollars?
　　　　　　　　　　　　　　　　　- Yes, 　　　　　.

4 The man wants to be a hairdresser.　　　　(현재, 과거)

　　의문문　　　　　　　　　　　　to be a hairdresser?
　　　　　　　　　　　　　　　　　- No, 　　　　　.

5 The visitors saw the high tower.　　　　　(현재, 과거)

　　부정문　　　　　　　　　　　　the high tower.

6 Jane had a good time.　　　　　　　　　(현재, 과거)

　　부정문　　　　　　　　　　　　a good time.

7 He took an umbrella.　　　　　　　　　(현재, 과거)

　　의문문　　　　　　　　　　　　an umbrella?
　　　　　　　　　　　　　　　　　- Yes, 　　　　　.

8 You(너는) felt a chill.　　　　　　　　(현재, 과거)

　　의문문　　　　　　　　　　　　a chill?
　　　　　　　　　　　　　　　　　- Yes, 　　　　　.

9 Leaves change their color in fall.　　　　(현재, 과거)

　　부정문　　　　　　　　　　　　their color in fall.

10 He sat on his seat.　　　　　　　　　(현재, 과거)

　　의문문　　　　　　　　　　　　on his seat?
　　　　　　　　　　　　　　　　　- No, 　　　　　.

way 길
forest 숲
introduce 소개하다
believe 믿다
cost (비용이) 들다
feel a chill 한기를 느끼다.
leaves leaf(나뭇잎)의 복수
fall 가을
seat 좌석, 자리

Unit 04 81

다음 밑줄 친 부분들 중에서 틀린 곳을 바르게 고쳐 써 보자.

ago ~전에
band 악단
pocket (옷의) 주머니
essay 수필
lose 잃다
luaggage (여행용) 짐
field 들판

1 These <u>was</u> beautiful flowers a week <u>ago</u>.
were

2 He <u>didn't</u> <u>works</u> hard last night.

3 Jane <u>were</u> a <u>singer</u> of the band before.

4 Wendy <u>putted</u> her hand in <u>her pocket</u>.

5 <u>Did</u> they <u>found</u> a tiger?

6 <u>The teacher</u> <u>had not</u> a nice car then.

7 My aunt <u>reads</u> an essay two <u>years</u> ago.

8 Mary <u>didn't</u> <u>visits</u> her friend last sunday.

9 I <u>lost not</u> my <u>luggage</u> ten minutes ago.

10 They <u>don't</u> <u>come</u> back last Sunday.

11 <u>Does</u> she <u>go</u> to the pet shop yesterday?

12 The tomatoes <u>are</u> very <u>fresh</u> yesterday morning.

13 Did <u>Joe</u> <u>lived</u> to play tennis?

14 The soldiers <u>was</u> <u>in</u> the field then.

15 I <u>selled</u> my <u>old</u> car yesterday.

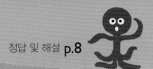

2

다음 밑줄 친 부분들 중에서 <u>틀린</u> 곳을 바르게 고쳐 써 보자.

1 They <u>lie</u> down <u>on</u> the grass two hours ago.
   lay

2 Mr. Kim <u>sended</u> a lot of pictures <u>to</u> James last year.

3 He <u>does not</u> <u>turn off</u> the radio yesterday morning.

4 <u>We</u> <u>make</u> an apple pie last week.

5 <u>Did</u> he <u>kind</u> and wise then?

6 The barber <u>cuts</u> his <u>son's</u> hair an hour ago.

7 <u>Did</u> you <u>spent</u> the money last week?

8 Tom <u>did</u> not <u>rubs</u> softly.

9 The boy <u>doesn't</u> get up <u>early</u> yesterday morning.

10 <u>They</u> didn't <u>got</u> there.

11 I <u>had not</u> <u>any</u> friends 3 years ago.

12 I <u>did</u> not a director 10 years <u>ago</u>.

13 She <u>slept</u> in her room <u>yesterday</u> morning.

14 <u>Where</u> <u>are</u> your brothers last night?

15 He <u>hits</u> <u>the door</u> yesterday.

lie down 드러눕다
lay lie (눕다)의 과거
two hours ago 2시간 전에
turn off ~을 끄다
apple pie 사과 파이
rub 문지르다
director 감독
shelf 선반

01 다음 우리말과 같은 뜻이 되도록 할 때, 빈칸에 들어갈 말로 알맞은 것은?

더 알아보기

> 내 사촌은 휴대폰을 사지 않았다.
>
> → My cousin _____ buy a cell phone.

① doesn't   ② don't

③ didn't   ④ weren't

⑤ wasn't

01
cell phone 휴대폰

02 다음은 민호의 어제 일과를 나타낸 것이다. 이와 어울리지 <u>않는</u> 것은?

> ⓐ I got up at eight o'clock.
>
> ⓑ I didn't eat breakfast.
>
> ⓒ I played soccer after school.
>
> ⓓ I take a shower.
>
> ⓔ I did my homework before sleeping.

① ⓐ   ② ⓑ

③ ⓒ   ④ ⓓ

⑤ ⓔ

02
주어진 문장들은
어제의 일과이므로
과거형으로 표현해야
한다.

03 다음 빈칸에 공통으로 들어갈 말로 알맞은 것은?

A : What _____ you do yesterday?

B : I slept all day.

A : He met Susan last month.

B : Really? I _____ not meet her then.

① do
② didn't
③ did
④ were
⑤ was

더 알아보기

03
문장 끝에 과거를 나타내는 부사 yesterday가 있고 대답의 시제가 과거이다.

04 다음 질문에 대한 대답으로 알맞은 것은? (2개)

A : Was your son late for school?

B : _____

① Yes, he is.
② No, he isn't.
③ Yes, he was.
④ Yes, he were.
⑤ No, he wasn't.

05 다음 문장 중 바른 것은?

① Tom didn't builds his house.
② Did she stays in Seoul?
③ He didn't meets his teacher.
④ My mother didn't goes to the bank.
⑤ Did Jane call her mother?

[06–07] 다음 문장을 부정문으로 바꿔 쓰시오.

06
They were happy then.

→ _____

07
My brother broke the window.

→ _____

08 다음 대화의 빈칸에 들어갈 말로 알맞은 것은?

> A : Did you have dinner with Bill yesterday?
>
> B : _____

① Yes, I do.   ② No, I don't.
③ No, I didn't.   ④ Yes, I didn't.
⑤ No, I haven't.

09 다음 문장에서 <u>틀린</u> 부분을 바르게 고쳐 쓰시오.

> Did you made a chair?

_____ ⇨ _____

10 다음 문장을 과거형의 부정문으로 바르게 바꿔 쓴 것은?

> He plays golf.

① He plays golf.
② He don't played golf.
③ He didn't plays golf.
④ He didn't played golf.
⑤ He didn't play golf.

다음 문장을 지시대로 바꿔 보자. 의문문은 대답도 써 보자.

1 The soldier was very brave. brave 용감한

의문문 _____ very brave?

– Yes, _____

2 She wanted to visit her mother.

부정문 _____ to visit her mother.

3 He heard his son's voice.

의문문 _____ his son's voice?

– No, _____

4 Susan opened her mind. mind 마음

의문문 _____ her mind?

– Yes, _____

5 Mr. Kim and Mrs. Kim sold a lot of pears.

부정문 _____ a lot of pears.

6 We were free then. free 한가한

부정문 _____ free then.

7 Your sister memorized Tom's address. memorize 외우다 address 주소

의문문 _____ Tom's address?

– Yes, _____

8 The girl understood the question.

부정문 _____ the question.

9 This dog swam well.

부정문 _____ well.

10 Inho listened to music.

의문문 _____ to music?

– No, _____

Grammar **Joy** 4

- **Review Test 1**
- **내신대비 1**

01   다음 중 알맞은 것을 골라 동그라미 해 보자.

1   He has (three, third) caps.

2   She writes her (seven, seventh) book.

3   This is my (four, fourth) trip to China.

4   I need (one, first) hour more.

5   May is the (five, fifth) month of the year.

6   They won (six, sixth) games in a row.   in a row 연속해서

7   Today is the (two, second) day of this month.

02   다음 중 알맞은 것을 골라 동그라미 해 보자.

1   1988   (nineteen eighty-eight, nineteen eight-eight)

2   8월 20일   (twenty August, August twenty)

3   010-3109-xxxx

     (zero one oh-three one oh nine-, oh one zero-three one zero nine-)

4   25.74   (two five point seven four, twenty-five point seven four)

5 $12.68   (twelve dollars sixty eight cents, twelve dollars six eight cents)

6 $\frac{2}{3}$ (two third, two thirds)

7   6월 25일 일요일   (Sunday June twenty-fifth, twenty-fifth June Sunday)

03 다음 ( ) 안의 숫자를 기수 또는 서수로 써 보자.

1 She has _____ pens. (15)

2 This is _____ tunnel. (2) tunnel 터널

3 He exercises _____ hour everyday. (1)

4 Tom is in _____ grade. (5)

5 I am _____ years old. (11)

6 There are _____ seasons in a year. (4)

7 My classroom is on _____ floor. (3)

04 다음 숫자를 영어로 써 보자.

1 35.12   thirty five point _____

2 2월 24일   February _____

3 $20.15   _____ dollars _____ cents

4 $\dfrac{3}{5}$ three _____

5 2015   two _____

6 010-5730-xxxx   _____ one _____ five _____ three _____ -

7 1817년 7월 5일   _____ five _____

01 다음 중 알맞은 것을 골라 동그라미 해 보자.

1 (How, What) is the weather ?   – It is sunny.

2 What (day, date, time) is it ?   – It is 5 o'clock.

3 What (day, date, time) is it ?   – It is Wednesday.

4 What (day, date, time) is it ?   – It is January 2nd.

5 What (day, date, time) do you have?   – It is noon.

6 Do you have (time, the time) ?   – It is 8 : 20.

7 (How, What) is the weather like?   – It is hot.

8 Do you have (time, the time) ?   – No, I am busy now.

02 다음 빈칸을 숫자로 채우고, (   ) 안에서 알맞은 말을 골라 보자.

1 It's two fifty.   [   ] 시 [   ] (분, 분 전)입니다.

2 It's nine oh seven.   [   ] 시 [   ] (분, 분 전)입니다.

3 It's six to seven.   [   ] 시 [   ] (분, 분 전)입니다.

4 It's a quarter to three.   [   ] 시 [   ] (분, 분 전)입니다.

5 It's half past ten.   [   ] 시 [   ] (분, 분 전)입니다.

03 다음 대화의 빈칸에 알맞은 말을 써 보자.

1 _____ _____ is it now?　　　　　– It is 3 o'clock.

2 _____ _____ is it?　　　　　– It is Friday .

3 _____ _____ is it?　　　　　– It's June 12.

= _____ is the _____ ?

4 _____ is the weather like?　　　　　– It's snowy.

= _____ is the weather?

5 What time _____ you _____ ?　　　　　– It's eleven oh five.

04 다음 빈칸을 채우고 영어로 나타내보자.

1 08 : 40 = _____ 시 _____ 분 전

⇨ It's _____ _____

⇨ It's _____ to _____

2 11 : 50 = _____ 시 _____ 분 전

⇨ It's _____ _____

⇨ It's _____ to _____

3 09 : 15

⇨ It's _____ _____

⇨ It's _____ past _____

4 02 : 30

⇨ It's _____ _____

⇨ It's _____ past _____

5 자정 밤12 : 00 (1가지)

⇨ It's _____

01 우리말에 알맞은 동사를 골라 동그라미 해 보자.

1 He (is, are, was, were) sick last month.   그는 지난달에 아팠었다.

2 I (is, are, was, were) busy then.   나는 그때 바빴다.

3 They (is, are, was, were) poor.   그들은 가난했다.

4 We (is, are, was, were) students.   우리는 학생들이다.

5 Susan (is, are, was, were) at home.   Susan은 집에 있었다.

6 The puppy (is, are, was, were) cute.   그 강아지는 귀엽다.

7 This tree (is, are, was, were) short before.   이 나무는 전에 작았다.

02 우리말에 알맞은 동사를 골라 동그라미 해 보자.

1 Tom (cleans, cleaned, is cleaning) his room yesterday.
Tom은 어제 그의 방을 청소했다.

2 Jane (studies, studied, is studying) English every day.
Jane 은 매일 영어를 공부한다.

3 I (visit, visited, is visiting) my grandmother last week.
나는 지난 주 할머니를 방문했다.

4 She (swims, swam, is swimming) now.
그녀는 지금 수영을 하고 있는 중이다.

5 They (play, played, are playing) basketball last Sunday.
그들은 지난 일요일에 농구를 했다.

03 문장의 시제를 고르고, 주어진 동사를 우리말에 알맞게 바꿔 보자.

1 Jane _____ slim in a kid. (is)　　　(현재, 과거)

Jane은 꼬마였을 때 말랐었다.

2 Mom _____ a teacher. (is)　　　(현재, 과거)

엄마는 선생님이었다.

3 I _____ tired now. (am)　　　(현재, 과거)

나는 지금 피곤하다.

4 They _____ happy. (are)　　　(현재, 과거)

그들은 행복했다.

5 Uncle _____ always busy. (is)　　　(현재, 과거)

삼촌은 항상 바쁘다.

04 주어진 동사를 우리말에 알맞게 바꿔 보자.

1 Tom _____ home just now.(come)　　　(현재, 현재 진행, 과거)

Tom은 방금 전에 집에 왔다.

2 We _____ the exam last month. (take)　　　(현재, 현재 진행, 과거)

우리는 지난 달 시험을 보았다.

3 It _____ now. (snow)　　　(현재, 현재 진행, 과거)

지금 눈이 오고 있는 중이다.

4 She _____ two pens. (buy)　　　(현재, 현재 진행, 과거)

그녀는 펜 2 개를 샀다.

5 He _____ a dog. (have)　　　(현재, 현재 진행, 과거)

그는 개 한 마리가 있다.

O1 다음 문장을 지시대로 바꿔 보자.

1 He was happy.

부정문 ☐☐☐☐ happy.

2 She was a doctor.

의문문 ☐☐☐☐ a doctor?

3 They were hungry.

부정문 ☐☐☐☐ happy.

4 The game was interesting.

의문문 ☐☐☐☐ interesting?

5 There was an eraser in the pencil case.

부정문 ☐☐☐☐ an eraser in the pencil case.

O2 다음 문장을 지시대로 바꿔 보자.

1 They liked PC games.

부정문 ☐☐☐☐ PC games.

2 Tom went to China.

의문문 ☐☐☐☐ to China?

3 I had a bike.

부정문 ☐☐☐☐ a bike.

4 She sold a lot of apples.

의문문 ☐☐☐☐ a lot of apples?

5 Her family lived in London.

부정문 ☐☐☐☐ in London.

03 다음 질문에 대답을 완성해 보자.

1 Was he a dentist? Yes, _____ _____.

2 Did she wear a coat? Yes, _____ _____.

3 Did they save a lot of money? No, _____ _____.

4 Were the girls surprised? No, _____ _____.

5 Was the test difficult? Yes, _____ _____.

6 Did Nancy fly an airplane? No, _____ _____.

7 Was Jake hungry? Yes, _____ _____.

8 Did Tom have a cellphone? No, _____ _____.

9 Were they rich? Yes, _____ _____.

10 Did you make tea? No, _____ _____.

01 다음 중 성격이 <u>다른</u> 것은?

① third
② fifth
③ eleventh
④ twenty
⑤ second

02 다음 숫자를 영어의 기수와 서수로 써 보세요.

> 4

기수 : _____   서수 : _____

03 다음을 바르게 읽은 것은?

> 32.75 kg

① thirty-two point seventy-five kilograms
② thirty-two point seven five kilograms
③ three two point seven five kilograms
④ three two point seventy-five kilograms
⑤ thirty-two point seventy fifth kilograms

04 다음 분수를 차례로 바르게 읽은 것을 연결한 것은?

> $\dfrac{5}{9}$ – $\dfrac{1}{2}$

① five-nine - a half
② fifth-nine - one half
③ five-ninths - a half
④ fifth-ninth - one half
⑤ five-nines - half

05 다음 년도를 차례로 바르게 읽은 것은?

> 1992 – 2018

① nineteen ninety-two
  - two thousand eighteen
② nineteen ninety-two
  - two thousand one eight
③ nineteen nine-two
  - two thousand eighteen
④ nineteen nine-second
  - two thousand one eight
⑤ nineteen ninety-second
  - two thousand eighteen

6 다음을 영어로 써 보세요.

$$5 \frac{2}{9} : \underline{\hspace{4cm}}$$

5와 9분의 2

7 다음에서 It의 쓰임이 보기와 <u>다른</u> 것은?

It is December 23rd.

① It is 7 o'clock.
② It is Sunday.
③ It is my pen.
④ It is cold.
⑤ It is dark.

8 다음 빈칸에 알맞은 말을 써 보세요.

How is the weather?
= _____ is the weather like?

09 다음 대답에 대한 질문으로 알맞지 <u>않은</u> 것은?

It is 5 o'clock.

① What time is it?
② Do you have the time?
③ What time do you have?
④ Do you have time?
⑤ What time is it now?

10 다음 대답에 대한 질문으로 알맞은 것을 빈칸에 써 보세요.

A : What _____ is it there?
B : It is summer here.

11 다음 주어진 시각을 영어로 나타낼 때, 빈칸에 들어갈 말이 순서대로 바르게 짝지어진 것은?

8시 40분 : eight _____
twenty _____ nine

① forty - past
② forty - after
③ forty - to
④ four oh - for
⑤ four oh - by

12 다음 주어진 시각을 영어로 나타낸 것이다. 빈칸에 알맞게 써 보자.

> 2시 15분
> · two _____
> · _____ after two
> · _____ past two

13 다음 중 동사의 과거형이 바르게 연결되지 않은 것을 골라 보자.

① come - came
② go - went
③ buy - bought
④ teach - thought
⑤ is - was

14 다음 빈칸에 공통으로 들어갈 말로 알맞은 것은?

> Uncle was busy _____.
> I bought a cap _____.

① next week
② tomorrow
③ in two hours
④ now
⑤ last week

in two hours 2시간 후에

15 다음 문장을 과거형으로 바꿀 때, 올바른 것은?

> Tom reads a novel.

① Tom readed a novel.
② Tom was read a novel.
③ Tom read a novel.
④ Tom was reading a novel.
⑤ Tom did reads a novel.

novel 소설

16 다음 어법상 옳지 않은 것은?

① Jane met her old friend last week.
② Jane called me last week.
③ Jane buys a doll last week.
④ Jane enjoyed swimming last week.
⑤ Jane was sick last week.

enjoy 즐기다

17 다음 문장의 시제에 맞도록 (   ) 안의 동사를 바르게 바꿔 보자.

> I _____ tired yesterday. (am)
>
> He _____ his wallet last week. (lose)

8 다음 빈칸에 들어갈 말이 <u>다른</u> 것은?

① _____ you clean your room yesterday?
② _____ he very busy last week?
③ _____ they go camping last summer?
④ _____ she arrive in L.A. last night?
⑤ _____ Jane buy the smart-phone last year?

9 다음 빈칸에 공통으로 들어갈 말로 알맞은 것은?

I _____ at the office this afternoon.
나는 오늘 오후에 사무실에 없었어.
There _____ anything on the table.
탁자위에는 아무 것도 없었다.

① didn't
② don't
③ doesn't
④ weren't
⑤ wasn't

20 틀린 곳을 찾아 바르게 고쳐 써 보자.

> Do she busy yesterday?

_____ ⇨ _____

21 다음 우리말 해석이 알맞은 것은?

> He didn't break the glass.

① 그는 그 유리컵을 깨지 않는다.
② 그는 그 유리컵을 깨지 않아야 한다.
③ 그는 그 유리컵을 깨지 않을 것이다.
④ 그는 그 유리컵을 깨지 않을 수 있다.
⑤ 그는 그 유리컵을 깨지 않았다.

22 다음을 부정문으로 바꿔 쓸 때, 빈칸에 알맞은 말을 쓰시오.

> Jane did the work.
> → Jane _____ _____ the work.

23 다음 빈칸에 들어갈 말이 나머지와 <u>다른</u> 것은?

① _____ she leave Korea last week?

② _____ you see Bill yesterday?

③ _____ Jane sick last month?

④ _____ Tom help mom last night?

⑤ _____ they open the store last month?

24 다음 질문에 대한 대답이 차례대로 알맞은 것은?

> A : Was Jane upset yesterday?
>
> B : No, _____ .
>
> A : Did they arrive at the airport?
>
> B : Yes, _____ .

① she isn't. - they did

② she wasn't - they didn't

③ she weren't - they do

④ she wasn't - they did

⑤ she didn't - they were

25 다음을 의문문으로 바꿔 쓸 때, 빈칸에 알맞은 말을 쓰시오.

> Tom has a lot of coins.
>
> → _____ _____ _____
>
> a lot of coins?

Unit o5

과거진행형

과거의 한 시점에서 진행하고 있던 일을
표현하는 말로,
「~하는 중이었다. ~하고 있었다」
라는 뜻을 가진다.

Unit 05 과거진행형

과거진행형이란?

과거에 한 시점에서 진행하고 있던 일을 표현하는 말로, 「~하는 중이었다, ~하고 있었다」의 뜻이다.

1 과거진행형 만들기

현재진행형의 be동사만 과거형을 써 주면 된다.

> 과거 be동사(was, were) + 동사원형 -ing

단수			복수		
I	was		We		
You	were	~ing.	You	were	~ing.
He, She, It	was		They		

ex. I am calling Jane.　　나는 Jane에게 전화하고 있다.
I **was** calling Jane.　　나는 Jane에게 전화하고 있었다.

2 부정문

be동사 뒤에 **not**을 붙여서 부정문을 만든다.

단수			복수		
I	was not		We		
You	were not	~ing.	You	were not	~ing.
He, She, It	was not		They		

ex. I was working then.　　나는 그 때 일하고 있었다.
I **was not working** then.　　나는 그 때 일하고 있지 않았다.

의문문

was/were를 주어 앞으로 보내고 문장 끝에 물음표(?) 붙여서 의문문을 만든다.

단수			복수		
Was	I			we	
Were	you	~ing?	Were	you	~ing?
Was	he, she, it			they	

ex. **He was sending** an e-mail.   그는 이메일을 보내고 있었다.
     Was he sending an e-mail?   그는 이메일을 보내고 있었니?

Yes, No로 대답하고, was/were로 질문하므로 **was/were**로 받으면 된다.

ex. **Were** you cleaning your room? 너는 너의 방을 치우고 있었니?

   – Yes, I **was.**   응. 그랬어.

   – No, I **was not.**   아니. 그렇지 않았어.

각 시제에 따른 쓰임

1 현재형

▶ 일반적인 사실과 습관을 나타낼 때

   ex. I **study** English every day.   나는 매일 영어를 공부한다.

▶ 변하지 않는 진리나 속담 ,격언을 말할 때

   ex. Health **is** better than wealth.   건강이 부보다 낫다.

2 현재진행형

▶ 지금 하고 있는 동작을 나타낼 때

   ex. I **am studying** English now.   나는 지금 영어를 공부하는 중이다.

3 과거진행형

▶ 과거의 한 시점에서 하고 있던 동작을 나타낼 때

   ex. I **was studying** English then.   나는 그 때 영어를 공부하는 중이었다.

*미래 시제는 unit6에서 배우기로 한다.

다음 문장에서 동사에 동그라미 하고 시제를 고른 후, 우리말로 옮겨 보자.

walk a dog 개를 산책시키다.

1 I (was learning) English. (현재진행형, (과거진행형))

⇨ 나는 영어를 배우고 있는 중이었다

I am learning English. ((현재진행형), 과거진행형)

⇨ 나는 영어를 배우고 있는 중이다

2 We are walking a dog. (현재 진행형, 과거진행형)

⇨ 우리는 개를

We were walking a dog. (현재 진행형, 과거진행형)

⇨ 우리는 개를

3 He is having dinner. (현재 진행형, 과거진행형)

⇨ 그는 저녁을

He was having dinner. (현재 진행형, 과거진행형)

⇨ 그는 저녁을

4 They were working. (현재 진행형, 과거진행형)

⇨ 그들은

They are working. (현재 진행형, 과거진행형)

⇨ 그들은

5 It is snowing. (현재 진행형, 과거진행형)

⇨ 눈이

It was snowing. (현재 진행형, 과거진행형)

⇨ 눈이

2

다음 문장을 과거진행형으로 바꿔 보자.

1 I fix the printer.

⇨ I _____*was fixing*_____ the printer.

2 Judy and David skate in the ice rink.

⇨ Judy and David _____ in the ice rink.

3 We plant an apple tree.

⇨ We _____ an apple tree.

4 Sara bakes some bread in the toaster.

⇨ Sara _____ some bread in the toaster.

5 He stands in the doorway.

⇨ He _____ in the doorway.

6 The tiger eats some meat.

⇨ The tiger _____ some meat.

7 You watch your children.

⇨ You _____ your children.

8 Your friend laughs at Minho.

⇨ Your friend _____ at Minho.

9 I hold my tongue.

⇨ I _____ my tongue.

10 A lot of Chinese exercise in the park.

⇨ A lot of Chinese _____ in the park.

printer 프린터
ice rink 스케이트장
toaster 토스터
doorway 출입구
meat 고기
laugh 웃다
hold 잡다
tongue 혀
hold one's tongue 잠자코
있다.
Chinese 중국인
exercise 운동하다

다음 문장의 시제를 고른 후, 주어진 단어를 우리말에 알맞게 바꿔 보자.

snore 코를 골다
make tea 차를 준비하다
(만들다)
cough 기침하다
spend 소비하다
summer vacation 여름휴가
surf on the Internet
인터넷에서 검색하다
give a speech 연설하다
make a fire 불을 지피다

1 나의 아빠는 지금 코를 골고 있다. (snore)　　(현재진행), 과거진행)

⇨ My dad　　*is snoring*　　now.

2 수진이와 나는 차를 준비하고 있었다. (make)　　(현재진행, 과거진행)

⇨ Sujin And I　　　　　　tea.

3 그 아이들은 원숭이들을 바라보고 있는 중이다. (look)　　(현재진행, 과거진행)

⇨ The children　　　　　　at the monkey.

4 나는 친구들과 야구를 하고 있다. (play)　　(현재진행, 과거진행)

⇨ I　　　　　　basketball with my friends.

5 그는 그때 기침을 하고 있었다. (cough)　　(현재진행, 과거진행)

⇨ He　　　　　　then.

6 나의 가족은 여름휴가를 보내는 중이다. (spend)　　(현재진행, 과거진행)

⇨ My family　　　　　　summer vacation.

7 그는 인터넷에서 검색중이다. (surf)　　(현재진행, 과거진행)

⇨ He　　　　　　on the Internet.

8 엄마와 아빠는 홀에서 연설하고 있었다. (give)　　(현재진행, 과거진행)

⇨ Mom and dad　　　　　　a speech in the hall.

9 그 불쌍한 거지는 길 위에서 죽어가고 있었다. (die)　　(현재진행, 과거진행)

⇨ The poor beggar　　　　　　on the street.

10 우리들은 불을 지피고 있었다. (make)　　(현재진행, 과거진행)

⇨ We　　　　　　a fire.

2

다음 문장의 시제를 고른 후, 주어진 단어를 우리말에 알맞게 바꿔 보자.

1 그는 영화를 보는 중이었다. (watch) (현재진행, 과거진행)

⇨ He _was watching_ drama.

2 Tom은 그 때 타자를 치는 중이었다. (type) (현재진행, 과거진행)

⇨ Tom _____ then.

3 그녀는 그녀의 친구들과 함께 커피를 마시고 있었다. (drink) (현재진행, 과거진행)

⇨ She _____ coffee with her friends.

4 많은 사람들이 공원에서 조깅하고 있다. (jog) (현재진행, 과거진행)

⇨ Many people _____ at Park.

5 Tom과 Judy는 채팅을 하고 있다. (chat) (현재진행, 과거진행)

⇨ Tom and Judy _____ .

6 우리는 그 때 보고서를 쓰는 중이었다. (write) (현재진행, 과거진행)

⇨ We _____ a report then.

7 엄마는 MSG대신에 설탕을 사용하고 있다. (use) (현재진행, 과거진행)

⇨ Mother _____ sugar instead of MSG.

8 그들은 거실에서 잠자고 있다. (sleep) (현재진행, 과거진행)

⇨ They _____ in the living room.

9 나는 7시로 알람 시계를 맞추고 있다. (set) (현재진행, 과거진행)

⇨ I _____ the alarm clock at 7.

10 Matt는 누군가를 쫓고 있다. (chase) (현재진행, 과거진행)

⇨ Matt _____ someone.

type 타자를 치다
instead of ~대신에
living room 거실
set the alarm clock
자명종 시계를 맞추다
chase 쫓다
someone 누군가

Unit 05 109

다음 문장을 지시대로 바꿔 보자.

1 He was playing the flute.

부정문 _He_   _wasn't_   _playing_ the flute.

2 Your daughter was washing her sneakers.

의문문   her sneakers?

3 I was doing the laundry.

부정문   the laundry.

4 Your aunt was peeling the apple.

의문문   the apple?

5 They were taking a test at that time.

부정문   a test at that time.

6 Many people were running away from there.

의문문   away from there?

7 Two taxis were coming.

의문문   ?

8 Maria was making her bed.

부정문   her bed.

9 John was pouring hot water into the bottle.

의문문   hot water into the bottle?

10 Bill and his friend were playing cards.

부정문   cards.

sneakers 운동화
do the laundry 빨래하다
peel 껍질을 벗기다
take a test 시험을 치르다
at that time 그 당시에
run away 도망치다
pour 붓다

4

다음 질문에 Yes와 No로 시작하는 대답을 완성해 보자.

1 Was she preparing dinner?

– No, _she_ _wasn't_ .

2 Were they crying?

– No, .

3 Were the boys meeting the celebrity?

– Yes, .

4 Was your mom shopping at the mall?

– Yes, .

5 Were you(너는) studying without a tutor?

– No, .

6 Was he holding a cane?

– Yes, .

7 Were Tom and Jim talking together?

– No, .

8 Was a stranger leaning on you in the subway?

– No, .

9 Was your grandmother sewing?

– Yes, .

10 Were your parents dancing together?

– Yes, .

prepare 준비하다
celebrity 연예인
tutor 과외교사
cane 지팡이
hold 잡다
lean on ~에 기대다
stranger 낯선 사람

4 의문사 who가 주어로
쓰이면 단수 동사가 온다.

다음 밑줄 친 부분들 중에서 틀린 곳을 바르게 고쳐 써 보자.

poem 시
magazine 잡지
wedding cake 웨딩케익
marathon 마라톤 대회
machine 기계

1 나는 말을 타는 중이었다.

I <u>am</u> <u>riding</u> a horse.
  was

2 그녀는 샌드위치를 먹고 있다.

She <u>were</u> <u>eating</u> a sandwich.

3 우리는 그 당시에 델리에서 약간의 빵을 사고 있었다.

We <u>were</u> <u>buy</u> some bread in the deli at that time.

4 그는 그 때 그녀의 시를 읽고 있었니?

<u>Does</u> he <u>reading</u> her poems then?

5 그녀는 음악을 듣고 있다.

She <u>were</u> <u>listening</u> to music.

6 Bill은 Jane과 함께 결혼 케익을 자르고 있었다.

Bill <u>was</u> <u>cut</u> the wedding cake with Jane.

7 사람들은 그 배우를 환영하고 있었다.

People <u>did</u> <u>greeting</u> the actor.

8 지금 그 모든 소녀들이 눈물을 흘리고 있다.

All the girls <u>were</u> <u>tearing</u> now.

9 지금 나의 여동생은 마라톤 대회에서 달리고 있다.

My sister <u>was</u> <u>running</u> in the marathon now.

10 나는 그 기계를 점검하고 있었다.

I <u>checking</u> up the <u>machine</u>.

2

다음 밑줄 친 부분들 중에서 **틀린** 곳을 바르게 고쳐 써 보자.

1 그녀는 목욕하고 있었니?

<u>Was</u> she <u>take</u> a bath?
taking

2 Joe는 휴식을 취하고 있지 않았다.

Joe <u>did</u> not <u>taking</u> a break time.

3 그들은 영어듣기 연습을 하고 있는 중이니?

<u>Were</u> they <u>practicing</u> English listening?

4 누가 내 컴퓨터를 사용하고 있었니?

<u>Who</u> <u>using</u> my computer?

5 그는 같은 호텔에서 머무르고 있다.

He <u>was</u> <u>staying</u> at the same hotel.

6 우리는 건강을 위해 매일 운동을 한다.

We <u>were</u> <u>do</u> exercise for health everyday.

7 그들은 밖에서 놀고 있었니?

<u>Did</u> they <u>playing</u> outside?

8 Jane과 Susan은 그 시간에 스키를 타고 있지 않았다.

<u>Jane and Susan</u> <u>didn't</u> skiing at that time.

9 그 학생들은 몇 개의 책상을 나르는 중이었다.

The students <u>are</u> <u>carrying</u> some desks.

10 나는 너에게 미소짓고 있는 중이 아니었다.

I <u>weren't</u> <u>smiling</u> at you.

practice 연습하다
English listening 영어듣기
at that time 그 시간에
smile at ~에게 미소짓다

01 과거진행형 문장입니다. 다음 문장들에 공통으로 들어갈 수 있는 말은?

더알아보기

> · Jane _____ wearing a red cap.
>
> · Sam _____ keeping a hen.

① are
② is
③ was
④ were
⑤ do

02 다음 문장 중 옳은 것을 고르면?

① I were learning Chinese.
② He was working then.
③ She were driving to the mall.
④ We was swimming in the pool.
⑤ They was playing the violin.

02

Chinese 중국어

03 다음 우리말을 영어로 쓸 때, 빈칸에 알맞은 말은?

> Bill과 나는 그늘에서 쉬고 있는 중이었다.
>
> → Bill and I _____ a rest in the shade.

① am taking
② are taking
③ is taking
④ was taking
⑤ were taking

03

in the shade 그늘에서

04 다음 질문에 대한 대답으로 알맞은 것은?

A : was he drinking soda?

B : _____

① Yes, he is.   ② No, he isn't.
③ Yes, he was.   ④ He was.
⑤ He wasn't.

05 다음 문장을 부정문으로 바꿔 쓰시오.

We were making a snowman.

→ _____

05

snowman 눈사람

06 다음 문장 중 바른 것은?

① Was you playing the piano?
② I didn't learning music.
③ Mr. Kim was having dinner.
④ She was study science.
⑤ Was the girls cooking in the kitchen?

07 다음 빈칸에 들어갈 말로 알맞은 것은?

> They were skating in the pond _____.

① then
② tomorrow
③ next week
④ now
⑤ tomorrow evening

[08-09] 다음 문장을 과거진행형으로 바꿔 쓰시오.

08

> I am doing yoga in my room.
>
> → _____

08

do yoga 요가를 하다

09

> He and she wash their hands.
>
> → _____

10 다음 문장을 우리말로 옮길 때, 바르지 <u>않은</u> 것은?

① He is talking to Jim now.

→ 그는 지금 Jim에게 말하고 있다.

② The baby is sleeping well.

→ 그 아기는 잘 자고 있다.

③ Tom was doing his homework.

→ Tom은 그의 숙제를 하고 있었다.

④ She was selling a lot of strawberries.

→ 그녀는 많은 딸기를 팔고 있다.

⑤ I was painting the table.

→ 나는 그 탁자를 칠하고 있었다.

10

strawberry 딸기

정답 및 해설 p.11

주어진 단어를 우리말에 알맞게 바꿔 보자.

1 그녀는 그녀의 부츠를 광을 내고 있었다. (wax)

⇨ She _____ her boots.

2 그들은 영어로 말하고 있다. (speak)

⇨ They _____ in English.

3 우리는 유럽을 여행중이다. (travel)

⇨ We _____ in Europe.

4 그는 그의 개와 놀고 있는 중이었다. (play)

⇨ He _____ with his dog.

5 두 명의 어린이들이 길을 건너고 있는 중이었다. (cross)

⇨ Two children _____ the street.

6 그들은 구석에서 싸우고 있었다. (fight)

⇨ They _____ at the corner. corner 구석

7 그 새는 공중에서 날고 있었다. (fly)

⇨ The bird _____ in the air. in the air 공중에서

8 나는 나의 엄마에게 전화를 걸고 있다. (call)

⇨ I _____ my mom.

9 Jane은 그림을 그리는 중이었다. (draw)

⇨ Jane _____ a picture.

10 나의 아빠는 면도를 하고 있는 중이다. (shave) shave 면도를 하다

⇨ My daddy _____ .

Unit o6

미래형

미래형은 앞으로 일어날 일이나
계획을 말할 때 사용된다.
미래를 나타내는 표현에는
will과 be going to가 있다.

미래형

미래형이란?

앞으로 일어날 일이나 계획을 나타낼 때 사용되는 형태를 말한다. 미래를 나타내는 방법에는 조동사 will을 사용하는 것과 be going to를 사용하는 것이 있다.

1 will + 동사원형 (~할 것이다)

단수			복수		
I			We		
You	will	동사원형~.	You	will	동사원형~.
He, She, It			They		

ex. I **will help** him. 나는 그를 도울 것이다.

1 부정문 만들기

will 뒤에 not만 붙이면 된다.

단수			복수		
I			We		
You	will not	동사원형~.	You	will not	동사원형~.
He, She, It			They		

ex. I **won't** be a doctor. 나는 의사가 되지 않을 것이다.

* will not의 축약형은 won't이다.

2 의문문 만들기

will을 주어 바로 앞으로 보내고 물음표(?)만 붙이면 된다.

단수			복수		
	I			we	
Will	you	동사원형~?	Will	you	동사원형~?
	he, she, it			they	

Yes와 No로 대답하고 will로 질문하므로 will로 대답한다.

ex. **Will** you be at the party tonight? 오늘 밤 그 파티에 있을 거니?

     – Yes, I **will**. 응. 그럴거야.   – No, I **won't**. 아니, 그렇지 않을 거야.

be going to + 동사원형 (~할 예정이다)

단수			복수		
I	**am going to**	동사원형 ~.	We		동사원형 ~.
You	**are going to**		You	**are going to**	
He, She, It	**is going to**		They		

ex. I **am going to** meet him. 나는 그를 만날 예정이다.

1 부정문 만들기

be동사 뒤에 **not**을 붙이면 된다.

단수			복수		
I	am **not** going to	동사원형 ~.	We		동사원형 ~.
You	are **not** going to		You	are **not** going to	
He, She, It	is **not** going to		They		

ex. I **am not going to** meet him this evening. 나는 오늘 저녁에 그를 만나지 않을 예정이다.

2 의문문 만들기

be동사를 주어 바로 앞으로 보내고 물음표(?)만 붙이면 된다.

단수			복수		
Am	I	going to 동사원형~?	Are	we	going to 동사원형~?
Are	you			you	
Is	he, she, it			they	

yes와 No로 대답하고 be동사로 질문하므로 be동사로 대답한다.

ex. **Are you going to** meet him this evening? 오늘 저녁에 그를 만날 예정이니?

     – Yes, I **am**. 응. 그럴거야.   – No, I'm **not**. 아니, 그렇지 않을 거야.

미래를 나타내는 현재진행형

왕래발착동사(come, go, start, arrive, leave, …)는 부사구에 따라 현재진행형이 미래를 나타내기도 한다.

ex. He is coming home **now**. (현재)
　　그는 지금 집에 오고 있는 중이다.

　　He is coming home **next month**. (미래)
　　그는 다음 달에 집에 올 것이다.

 will과 be going to

will과 be going to는 둘다 미래를 나타낸다는 점에서 같은 의미의 표현으로 사용할 수 있다.

ex. I **will** take a trip. 나는 여행을 할 것이다.
　　 = I **am going to** take a trip.

▶ will과 be going to의 쓰임

조동사 will	be going to
가까운 미래	먼 미래
말하는 시점에 순간적으로 결정된 일을 말할 때 *ex.* You look very sick. I **will** help you. 　　피곤해 보인다. 내가 도와줄게.	미리 계획된 일이나 약속을 말할 때 *ex.* I **am going to** meet him this evening. 　　나는 오늘 저녁 그를 만나려고 한다.
변할 수 없는 객관적인 사실을 말할 때 *ex.* Sam **will** be 13 years old next year. 　　Sam은 내년에 열 세 살이 될 것이다. 　　~~Sam is going to be 13 years old~~ 　　~~next year.~~	

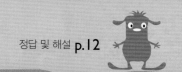

다음 문장에서 동사에 동그라미 하고 시제를 고른 후, 우리말로 옮겨 보자.

1 She will do her homework. (현재, 과거, **미래**)

⇨ 그녀는 그녀의 숙제를 *할 것이다.*

She did her homework. (현재, 과거, 미래)

⇨ 그녀는 그녀의 숙제를

She is going to do her homework. (현재, 과거, 미래)

⇨ 그녀는 그녀의 숙제를

She does her homework. (현재, 과거, 미래)

⇨ 그녀는 그녀의 숙제를

2 Tom reads a lot of books. (현재, 과거, 미래)

⇨ Tom은 많은 책을

Tom is going to read a lot of books. (현재, 과거, 미래)

⇨ Tom은 많은 책을

Tom read a lot of books. (현재, 과거, 미래)

⇨ Tom은 많은 책을

Tom will read a lot of books. (현재, 과거, 미래)

⇨ Tom은 많은 책을

3 My mom looked after him. (현재, 과거, 미래)

⇨ 나의 엄마는 그를

My mom looks after him. (현재, 과거, 미래)

⇨ 나의 엄마는 그를

My mom is going to look after him. (현재, 과거, 미래)

⇨ 나의 엄마는 그를

My mom will look after him. (현재, 과거, 미래)

⇨ 나의 엄마는 그를

look after 돌보다

다음 ( ) 안에서 알맞은 말을 골라 동그라미 해 보자.

1 He is going to (sing, sings) for Jane soon.

2 She will (be, is) a great designer.

3 We are going to (study, studies) math tomorrow.

4 I am going to (digs, dig) a hole.

5 It will (take, takes) two hours.

6 Mrs. Williams is going to (takes, take) a massage.

7 The king will (hunt, hunts) deer tomorrow.

8 They will (make, makes) kites.

9 The man (ride, rides) an elephant.

10 It will (be, are) Monday tomorrow.

11 She is going to (buy, buys) cheese pizza.

12 He will (is, be) at work.

13 Sam is going to (take, takes) a rest.

14 The butterfly will (fly, flies) up in the sky.

15 I will (capture, captures) the mosquito.

3

다음을 will을 이용하여 미래형으로 바꿔 보자.

1 I play soccer.
  ⇨ I   *will*   *play*   soccer.
2 My son calls me.
  ⇨ My son   me.
3 He is an actor.
  ⇨ He   an actor.
4 She is in the second grade.
  ⇨ She   in the second grade.
5 I am at home.
  ⇨ I   at home.

다음을 be going to를 이용하여 미래형으로 바꿔 보자.

1 It snows.
  ⇨ It   .
2 She takes a piano lesson next week.
  ⇨ She   a piano lesson next week.
3 Tom moves to America.
  ⇨ Tom   to America.
4 His daughter sees a dentist.
  ⇨ His daughter   a dentist.
5 My father pays for my coat.
  ⇨ My father   for my coat.

dentist 치과의사
pay for ~의 값을 지불하다

다음 두 문장의 뜻이 같도록 빈칸에 알맞은 말을 써 보자.

breakfast 아침 식사

1 They will take a subway.

= They _are_ _going_ _to_ _take_ a subway.

2 She is going to wear a red dress for the party.

= She _____ _____ a red dress for the party.

3 Mr. Baker will sell his old house.

= Mr. Baker _____ _____ _____ _____ his old house.

4 They will have breakfast.

= They _____ _____ _____ _____ breakfast.

5 You are going to talk to her.

= You _____ _____ to her.

6 Tom is going to get his friend's car.

= Tom _____ _____ his friend's car.

7 She will invite Jane.

= She _____ _____ _____ _____ Jane.

8 We will follow our teacher.

= We _____ _____ _____ _____ our teacher.

9 I am going to see a doctor.

= I _____ _____ a doctor.

10 She will exercise with Mr. Brown.

= She _____ _____ _____ _____ with Mr. Brown.

2

우리말에 알맞게 주어진 동사를 바꿔 보자.

1 He   *will play*   after school. (play)

그는 방과 후에 놀 것이다.

He   after school.   그는 방과 후에 놀았다.

He   after school.   그는 방과 후에 놀 예정이다.

He   after school.   그는 방과 후에 논다.

2 Tom   a photo of you. (take)

Tom은 너의 사진을 촬영한다.

Tom   a photo of you.   Tom은 너의 사진을 촬영할 것이다.

Tom   a photo of you.   Tom은 너의 사진을 촬영할 예정이다.

Tom   a photo of you.   Tom은 너의 사진을 촬영했다.

3 We   landscapes. (paint)

우리는 풍경화를 그릴 예정이다.

We   landscapes.   우리는 풍경화를 그렸다.

We   landscapes.   우리는 풍경화를 그린다.

We   landscapes.   우리는 풍경화를 그릴 것이다.

4 They   in Europe. (travel)

그들은 유럽을 여행할 것이다.

They   in Europe.   그들은 유럽을 여행할 예정이다.

They   in Europe.   그들은 유럽을 여행했다.

They   in Europe.   그들은 유럽을 여행한다.

다음 문장에서 시제를 고른 후, 우리말에 맞게 주어진 동사를 알맞은 형태로 바꿔 문장의 빈칸을 채워 보자. *(2가지 가능)*

soon 곧
compose 작곡하다

1 I *will(am going to) paint* my house. (paint) (현재, 과거, (미래))
나는 나의 집을 칠할 것이다.

2 He _____ her tonight. (call) (현재, 과거, 미래)
그는 오늘 밤 그녀에게 전화할 것이다.

3 We _____ many books during this summer vacation. (read) (현재, 과거, 미래)
우리는 이번 여름 방학동안 많은 책을 읽었다.

4 I _____ 14 years old next year. (be) (현재, 과거, 미래)
나는 내년에 14살이 될것이다.

5 They _____ this computer. (use) (현재, 과거, 미래)
그들은 이 컴퓨터를 사용한다.

6 The exam _____ difficult. (be) (현재, 과거, 미래)
그 시험은 어려웠다.

7 My father _____ smoking soon. (quit) (현재, 과거, 미래)
나의 아빠는 곧 담배를 끊을 것이다.

8 Jack _____ a lot of music. (compose) (현재, 과거, 미래)
Jack은 많은 음악을 작곡했다.

9 We _____ this weekend. (ski) (현재, 과거, 미래)
우리는 이번 주말에 스키 탈 것이다.

10 She always _____ for Jim. (wait) (현재, 과거, 미래)
그녀는 항상 그를 기다린다.

4

다음 문장에서 시제를 고른 후, 우리말에 맞게 주어진 동사를 알맞은
형태로 바꿔 문장의 빈칸을 채워 보자. (2가지 가능)

1 She _____ *bought* _____ school materials. (buy)

그녀는 준비물을 샀다. (현재, (과거), 미래)

2 Her bag is too heavy. I _____ it for her.
(carry) (현재, 과거, 미래)

그녀의 가방은 너무 무겁다. 나는 그녀를 위해 그것을 옮겨줄 거야.

3 I _____ an apple tree. (plant)

나는 사과나무 한그루를 심을 것이다. (현재, 과거, 미래)

4 Peter _____ Swiss. (travel) (현재, 과거, 미래)

peter는 스위스를 여행할 것이다.

5 She _____ some tea. (make)

그녀는 약간의 차를 준비했다. (현재, 과거, 미래)

6 It _____ stormy tomorrow. (be)

내일 폭풍우가 칠 것이다. (현재, 과거, 미래)

7 He _____ his mind. (open) (현재, 과거, 미래)

그는 그의 마음을 열었다.

8 They _____ up the church. (clean)

그들은 교회를 청소할 것이다. (현재, 과거, 미래)

9 She sometimes _____ olive oil. (use)

그녀는 가끔 올리브기름을 사용한다. (현재, 과거, 미래)

10 I _____ Susan's address. (memorize)

나는 susan의 주소를 기억하지 못한다. (현재, 과거, 미래)

school materials 준비물
mind 마음, 정신
stormy 폭풍(우)의
olive oil 올리브기름

다음 문장을 지시대로 바꿔 보자.

1 Tomorrow will be a busy day.

부정문 ▢Tomorrow▢ ▢won't▢ ▢be▢ a busy day.

2 She will skip dinner for diet.

의문문 ▢ ▢ ▢ dinner for diet?

3 Jane will wear an expensive bracelet at the party.

부정문 ▢ ▢ ▢ an expensive bracelet at the party.

4 I will eat a lot.

부정문 ▢ ▢ ▢ a lot.

5 They will sit around the campfire.

의문문 ▢ ▢ ▢ around the campfire?

다음 문장을 지시대로 바꿔 보자.

1 I am going to see a doctor.

부정문 ▢ ▢ ▢ ▢ ▢ ▢ a doctor.

2 He is going to sweep up dust.

부정문 ▢ ▢ ▢ ▢ ▢ ▢ up dust.

3 They are going to eat out tonight.

의문문 ▢ ▢ ▢ ▢ ▢ out tonight?

4 The cell phone is going to disappear.

부정문 ▢ ▢ ▢ ▢ ▢ .

5 You are going to take a break time in ten minutes.

의문문 ▢ ▢ ▢ ▢ ▢ a break time in ten minutes?

6

다음 질문에 Yes와 No로 시작하는 대답을 완성해 보자.

1 Will Tommy do his homework?
- Yes, *he* *will* .

2 Will they wax the floor?
- Yes, _____ _____ .

3 Will she be a designer?
- No, _____ _____ .

4 Will you(너는) be in Paris next week?
- No, _____ _____ .

5 Will you(너희들은) go hiking tomorrow morning?
- Yes, _____ _____ .

designer 디자이너
wax 광을 내다
speech 연설
copy 복사하다
tidy up 정리하다

다음 질문에 Yes와 No로 시작하는 대답을 완성해 보자.

1 Are you(너는) going to give a speech?
- Yes, _____ _____ .

2 Is she going to clean the bathroom?
- Yes, _____ _____ .

3 Is his brother going to copy this page?
- No, _____ _____ .

4 Is he going to take me home?
- No, _____ _____ .

5 Are Minsu and Tom going to tidy up their room?
- No, _____ _____ .

다음 밑줄 친 부분들 중에서 **틀린** 곳을 바르게 고쳐 써 보자.

plane 비행기
zoo 동물원
carpenter 목수
keep a diary 일기를 쓰다
tour 관광하다
watch 손목시계
cf. clock 괘종시계, 탁상시계
race 경주

9 변할 수 없는 객관적 사실

1 She <u>will</u> not <u>makes</u> any dresses.
　　　　　　　make

2 Mary <u>went to</u> the zoo tomorrow morning.

3 You will <u>are</u> a carpenter.

4 <u>My son</u> will <u>keeps</u> a diary.

5 I <u>going</u> to <u>tour</u> Europe next week.

6 He <u>willn't</u> <u>sell</u> his car.

7 <u>Are</u> you <u>go</u> to take the class?

8 She <u>is going</u> to <u>buys</u> a watch.

9 Jill <u>is going to</u> <u>be</u> seven years old.

10 Jimmy and Tim <u>are</u> <u>leave</u> for Seoul tomorrow morning.

11 He <u>is</u> going <u>turn</u> to the left.

12 Will she <u>is kind</u> to old men?

13 She <u>will</u> <u>wins</u> the race next year.

14 <u>Is</u> he going <u>have</u> breakfast with his mom?

15 I <u>am at</u> the bank tomorrow afternoon.

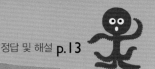

2

다음 밑줄 친 부분들 중에서 틀린 곳을 바르게 고쳐 써 보자.

1 She <u>be</u> a great artist <u>in</u> the future.
   will be

2 She <u>is</u> <u>go</u> to the beach this summer.

3 He <u>won't</u> <u>tells</u> a lie to you again.

4 <u>Is</u> you <u>going</u> to America to study next year?

5 My aunt is <u>going</u> buy me a computer game CD <u>tomorrow</u>.

6 My parents are <u>going</u> to <u>pays</u> for the shoes.

7 I <u>going</u> to <u>take</u> a shower later.

8 The concert <u>will</u> <u>ends</u> at 10 o'clock.

9 My friend <u>is</u> <u>arrive</u> at six.

10 The lawyer will <u>speaks</u> to the judge <u>for</u> us next week.

11 Mike and Tim <u>is</u> going <u>to wait</u> for us at the station.

12 She <u>is going to be</u> 20 years old next month.

13 I am <u>go</u> <u>to wear</u> this hat tomorrow.

14 <u>Did</u> you <u>visit</u> your grandparents next Saturday?

15 They <u>are</u> <u>go</u> to buy some cherries and oranges for us.

in the future 미래에
tell a lie 거짓말하다
aunt 이모, 고모
parents 부모님
judge 판사
station 역
hat 모자

O1 다음 중 not이 들어갈 위치로 알맞은 곳은?

> They ① are ② going ③ to ④ ride ⑤ a bike.

O2 다음 대화의 빈칸에 들어갈 말로 알맞은 것은?

> A : What are you going to do tomorrow?
>
> B : I _____ study English.

① go   ② am going to
③ went   ④ goes
⑤ are going to

O3 다음 빈칸에 들어갈 말로 알맞지 <u>않은</u> 것은?

> I will finish this work _____.

① tomorrow   ② soon
③ on Wednesday   ④ next week
⑤ last Saturday

04 다음 빈칸에 들어갈 말이 순서대로 바르게 짝지어진 것은?

> · He will _____ Jane.
>
> · Susan will _____ a good writer.

① meets - is   ② meet - is

③ meet - was   ④ meet - be

⑤ meet - were

05 다음 문장 중 바른 것은?

① The boy is going to opens the door.
② She is going to sings the song.
③ The baby is going to sleeps.
④ My family is going to eat out.
⑤ He is going to listens to music.

06 다음 두 문장의 뜻이 같도록 빈칸에 알맞은 말을 쓰시오.

> It will rain.
>
> = It _____ rain.

[07–08] 다음 질문에 대한 대답으로 알맞은 것을 고르시오.

07

> Is she going to meet Susan this Friday?

① Yes, she does.
② Yes, she was.
③ No, she isn't.
④ No, she doesn't.
⑤ No, she didn't.

08

> Will you help your mother?

① Yes, I am.
② Yes, I will.
③ No, I don't.
④ Yes, you will.
⑤ No, you don't.

09 다음 ( ) 안에서 알맞은 말을 고르시오.

He got up late yesterday.
He (will miss, missed) the train.

miss 놓치다, 그리워하다

10 다음 문장 중 바르지 <u>않은</u> 것은?

① I am going to is there this evening.
② He is going to see a movie.
③ He is going to have lunch.
④ I will be a scientist.
⑤ Sam is going to wash his car.

Quiz!

1, 2번은 will을, 3,4번은 be going to를 이용한 미래형 문장으로 만들고,
이 미래형 문장을 다시 의문문과 부정문으로 만들어 보자.

1 You are ten years old. ⇨ 미래형 _____

⇨ 의문문 _____

2 I help you ⇨ 미래형 _____

⇨ 부정문 _____

3 He plays Takwondo. ⇨ 미래형 _____

⇨ 부정문 _____

4 She sees a doctor. ⇨ 미래형 _____

⇨ 의문문 _____

다음 문장을 또 다른 표현을 이용한 미래형 문장으로 써 보자.

1 They will bring some books.

⇨ _____

2 Susan is going to meet him tonight.

⇨ _____

3 He is going to take a bus.

⇨ _____

4 I will wash the dishes.

⇨ _____

5 She is going to buy a computer.

⇨ _____

Unit **07**

감탄문

감탄문은 What과 How로 시작하는 것
두 종류가 있다. What으로 시작하는 감탄문은 'What
+a(n)+형용사+주어+동사!' 의 순서로,
How로 시작하는 감탄문은
'How+형용사(부사)+주어+동사!'의
순서로 온다.

감탄문

감탄문이란?

기쁨, 슬픔, 놀람, 희망 등의 감정을 나타낼 때 쓰는 문장을 말한다. 감탄문은 What이나 How로 시작하고 끝에 느낌표(!)를 붙인다.

1 What으로 시작하는 감탄문 만들기

What + a(an) + 형용사 + 명사 + 주어 + 동사!

He	is	a	very	great	pianist

그는 매우 훌륭한 피아니스트이다.

(very가 What으로 변신)

What	a	great	pianist	he	is!

형용사   명사   그는 얼마나 훌륭한 피아니스트인가!

1 감탄문으로 바꿀 때 **very**가 **what**으로 바뀌어 앞으로 나갈 경우, 단수 일 때 부정관사가 살아난다. 이 때 형용사의 첫 소리가 모음으로 소리 날 경우, 부정관사는 a가 아니라 an을 써야 한다.

ex. It is **a** very interesting book.   그것은 매우 재미있는 책이다.

→ What **an** interesting book it is!   그것은 얼마나 재미있는 책인지!

2 명사가 복수형으로 올 경우, 부정관사 (a/an)는 사용할 수 없다.

ex. They are very great pianists.   그들은 매우 훌륭한 음악가들이다.

→ What great pianists they are!

→ ~~What a great pianists they are!~~   그들은 얼마나 훌륭한 음악가들인지!

> **Tip!** very가 what이나 how로 바뀐다고 생각하고, 감탄문의 첫 글자를 따서
> 'What a 형명주동' / 'How 형주동'으로 외우면 쉽다.

2 How로 시작하는 감탄문 만들기

> **How** + 형용사/부사 + 주어 + 동사 !

The flower	is	very	beautiful

그 꽃은 매우 아름답다.

(very가 how로 변신)

How	beautiful	the flower	is!

형용사

그 꽃은 얼마나 아름다운지!

3 감탄문을 시작하는 what과 how

① very 뒤에 명사가 있으면 **What**으로 시작하는 감탄문을 만든다.

ex. He is a very fast runner.
　　주어 동사　　형용사　　명사

그는 매우 빠른 달리기 선수이다.

→ **What a fast runner** he is!
　　　형용사　　명사　　주어 동사

그는 얼마나 빠른 달리기 선수인지!

② very 뒤에 명사가 없을 때는 **How**로 시작하는 감탄문을 만든다.

ex. The boy runs very fast.
　　주어　　동사　　부사

그 소년은 매우 빨리 달린다.

→ **How** fast the boy runs!
　　부사　　주어 동사

그 소년은 얼마나 빨리 달리는지!

④ 감탄문 뒤에 오는 주어와 동사는 생략할 수 있다.

ex. What a nice day (it is)!　　얼마나 좋은 날인가!

How beautiful (she is)!　　얼마나 아름다운지!

> **Tip!** **감탄문과 의문문**
> 감탄문은 'How + 형용사' 뒤에 '주어 + 동사', 의문문은 '동사 + 주어'의 어순이 온다.
> How pretty <u>she</u> <u>is</u>! (감탄문)　　How pretty <u>is</u> <u>she</u>? (의문문)

다음 주어 동사를 지우고, 나머지에 명사가 있으면 동그라미하고, 알맞은 말을 골라 보자.

hungry 배고픈
pot 단지, 항아리, 냄비

* what 뒤에는
  「형용사+명사」가
  오고, how 뒤에는
  「형용사/부사」가 온다.

1 (What , How) a large farm this is!

2 (What, How) a hungry fox it is!

3 (What, How) sad the movie is!

4 (What, How) pretty flowers she has!

5 (What, How) well she runs!

6 (What, How) old clocks they are!

7 (What, How) handsome he is!

8 (What, How) sweet melons they are!

9 (What, How) a strong man his father is!

10 (What, How) difficult problems those are!

11 (What, How) famous Picasso is!

12 (What, How) exciting games these are!

13 (What, How) hot the pot is!

14 (What, How) nice the restaurants are!

15 (What, How) a small room this is!

2

주어진 문장을 감탄문으로 바꿔 보자.

1

| This doggy | is | very | cute. |

| How | cute | *this doggy* | *is!* |

doggy 강아지
cartoon book 만화책
fun 재미있는

2

| The girl | is | very | beautiful. |

| | | | |

3

| He | can swim | very | easily. |

| | | | |

4

| This cartoon book | is | very | fun |

| | | | |

5

| This | is | very | expensive. |

| | | | |

6

| You | look | very | happy. |

| | | | |

주어진 문장에서 very 뒤에 명사가 있으면 동그라미하고 감탄문으로
바꿔 보자.

Russia 러시아
country 나라
building 건물

1

This	is	a	very	sweet	orange.

What	a	sweet	orange	this	is!

2

These	are	very	sweet	oranges.

3

Russia	is	a	very	big	country.

4

Those	are	very	tall	buildings.

5

You	have	a	very	old	clock.

6

He	is	a	very	kind	clerk.

4

주어진 문장에서 very 뒤에 명사가 있으면 동그라미하고 감탄문으로 바꿔 보자.

dolphin 돌고래
perform 공연하다
wild 거친, 야생의

1

| That | is | a | very | exciting | game. |

| What | an | exciting | game | that | is! |

2

| He | made | a | very | delicious | cake. |

| | | | | | |

3

| Those | are | very | smart | dolphins. |

| | | | | |

4 주어+동사+목적어 +very~

| Judy | played | the cello | very | well. |

| | | | | |

5

| They | performed | very | nicely. |

| | | | |

6

| Tigers | are | very | wild. |

| | | | |

다음 ( ) 안의 단어를 바르게 배열하여 감탄문을 만들어 보자.

clever 영리한
lovely 사랑스러운, 아름다운
kitten 새끼고양이
poor 불쌍한
vase 꽃병

1 (You, boy, a, are, what, clever)!

⇨ *What a clever boy*   *you are* !

2 (her, was, long, hair, how)!

⇨   !

3 (how, feet, his, are, big)!

⇨   !

4 (strong, was, what, Samson, a, man)!

⇨   !

5 (those, sunflowers, tall, how, are)!

⇨   !

6 (these, what, lovely, dresses, are)!

⇨   !

7 (kitten, the, poor, is, how)!

⇨   !

8 (it, slow, how, goes)!

⇨   !

9 (what, she, an, was, teacher, excellent)!

⇨   !

10 (it, vase, cheap, what, a, is)!

⇨   !

2

다음 ( ) 안의 단어를 바르게 배열하여 감탄문을 만들어 보자.

1 (was, big, how, this, tower)!

⇨ | *How big* | *this tower was* | !

2 (the, is, oven, how, dangerous)!

⇨ | | | !

3 (is, great, a, what, artist, Picasso)!

⇨ | | | !

4 (a, what, it, day, fine, was)!

⇨ | | | !

5 (Bill Gates, is, how, rich)!

⇨ | | | !

6 (animals, are, bears, foolish, what)!

⇨ | | | !

7 (ugly, what, an, doll, is, that)!

⇨ | | | !

8 (speak, she, Japanese, can, how, well)!

⇨ | | | !

9 (shoes, these, a, what, are, dirty)!

⇨ | | | !

10 (is walking, he, slow, how)!

⇨ | | | !

tower 탑
dangerous 위험한
foolish 어리석은
animal 동물
ugly 못생긴
Japanese 일본사람, 일본어
slow 느린, 느리게

8 주어+동사+목적어
+very~

주어진 문장을 감탄문으로 바꿔 보자.

important 중요한
curry and rice 카레라이스
intelligent 머리가 좋은
turtle 거북이
heavy 무거운

3 주어+동사+목적어
+very~

1 It is a very important thing.

⇨ *What an important thing it is!*

2 Those are very important things.

⇨

3 She cooks curry and rice very fast.

⇨

4 They are very intelligent.

⇨

5 Jane has a very small face.

⇨

6 His mother is a very diligent woman.

⇨

7 This is a very deep lake.

⇨

8 This lake is very clean.

⇨

9 Turtles are very slow.

⇨

10 Those are very heavy boxes.

⇨

4

주어진 문장을 감탄문으로 바꿔 보자.

1 That is a very sweet pumpkin.

⇨ *What a sweet pumpkin that is!*

2 Mary looks very sad.

⇨

3 This is a very light jumper.

⇨

4 These are very wonderful boats.

⇨

5 This coffee is very hot.

⇨

6 I bought a very fashionable shirt.

⇨

7 This is a very sharp knife.

⇨

8 This room is very cold.

⇨

9 It is a very interesting story.

⇨

10 She is very full.

⇨

pumpkin 호박
light 가벼운
fashionable 유행하는
sharp 날카로운

다음 밑줄 친 부분들 중에서 틀린 곳을 바르게 고쳐 써 보자.

1 How sweet chocolate she made!
What

2 What skinny his sisters are!

3 What a old coat that is!

4 How a hungry the cat is!

5 What a lazy boys they are!

6 How a small face the movie star has!

7 How high jumped she!

8 What a delicious stew this is!

9 How good my sister can ski!

10 How a busy my mom is!

11 What handsome boy my nephew is!

12 What fresh these oranges are!

13 What salty this food is!

14 What a lovely children he is!

15 How a fat pig this is!

다음 밑줄 친 부분들 중에서 틀린 곳을 바르게 고쳐 써 보자.

1 <u>How</u> a warm sweater she <u>has</u>!
   What

2 What <u>a</u> easy game <u>it</u> is!

3 <u>How</u> great is the musician!

4 What <u>wise</u> <u>woman</u> they are!

5 <u>What</u> foggy <u>it</u> is!

6 <u>How</u> <u>an unkind</u> to her I was!

7 <u>What</u> famous <u>man</u> <u>he</u> is!

8 <u>What</u> sour these lemons <u>are</u>!

9 What <u>a</u> clean restaurant <u>is this</u>!

10 <u>How a</u> hard the pillow is!

11 <u>What</u> well she <u>plays</u> basketball!

12 What a <u>very</u> quiet city <u>this</u> is!

13 <u>What</u> sleepy I <u>am</u>!

14 <u>How</u> expensive cell phones they <u>are</u>!

15 <u>What</u> <u>an</u> hot onion that is!

musician 음악가
foggy 안개 낀
famous 유명한
pillow 베개
quiet 조용한

11 주어＋동사＋목적어
＋very～

01 다음 빈칸에 들어갈 말이 순서대로 바르게 짝지어진 것은?

> · _____ a big dinner this is!
>
> · _____ tired she looks!

① How - Why   ② What - When
③ What - How   ④ How - What
⑤ Who - What

02 다음 빈칸에 들어갈 말로 알맞지 <u>않은</u> 것은?

> What a _____ girl Susan is!

① beautiful   ② pretty
③ smart   ④ kind
⑤ happily

03 다음 문장을 감탄문으로 바꿔 쓰시오.

> Mary swims very well.
>
> → _____ !

04 다음 단어들을 배열하여 감탄문으로 만들 때, 올바른 순서는?

> (1) a, (2) house, (3) nice, (4) is, (5) this, (6) what

① (3)-(2)-(6)-(1)-(5)-(4)
② (6)-(1)-(3)-(2)-(5)-(4)
③ (6)-(3)-(2)-(1)-(4)-(5)
④ (6)-(1)-(3)-(5)-(4)-(2)
⑤ (5)-(4)-(1)-(3)-(2)-(6)

05 다음 문장을 감탄문으로 바꿀 때, <u>틀린</u> 부분을 바르게 고쳐 쓰시오.

> These are very old paintings.
>
> → How old paintings these are!

_____ ⇨ _____

05

형용사 old 뒤에
paintings라는 명사가
있음에 유의한다.

06 다음 문장 중 바르지 <u>않은</u> 것은?

① What a poor man he is!
② What big this pizza is!
③ How brave the boy is!
④ What a fine day it is!
⑤ How foolish the girls are!

07 다음 문장에서 바르지 <u>않은</u> 것은?

> What great painter they are!

① What
② they
③ great
④ painter
⑤ are

08 다음 문장의 빈칸에 올 수 있는 말을 |보기|에서 고르시오.

> | 보기 | ⓐ the train is   ⓑ is the train

(A) How long _____ ?

(B) How long _____ !

08
'How+형용사+주어+
동사!' 문장과 'How+
형용사+동사+주어?'
문장을 구분할 수
있어야 한다.

더알아보기

09 다음 빈칸에 들어갈 말로 알맞은 것은?

> What _____ bag this is!

① a expensive
② how expensive
③ an big
④ an expensive
⑤ the expensive

10 다음 문장을 감탄문으로 바꿔 쓰시오.

> My mother is very sick.
>
> → _____

10
very가 How로 바뀐다.

주어진 문장을 감탄문으로 바꿔 보자.

1 It is a very big elephant.

⇨

2 She is very short.

⇨

3 That is a very exciting game.

⇨

4 He has a very comfortable sofa. comfortable 편안한

⇨

5 They are very wonderful pictures!

⇨

6 My father looks very young.

⇨

7 Jim can play the cello very well.

⇨

8 The train is very long.

⇨

9 My sister is a very cute girl.

⇨

10 They are very busy.

⇨

Unit **O8**

부정의문문, 부가의문문

부정의문문은 부정의 형태로
묻는 문장을 말하며,
부가 의문문은 평서문 뒤에
짧게 덧붙여 묻는 의문문이다.

Unit 08

부정의문문, 부가의문문

부정의문문이란?
'~하지 않아?' 하고 부정으로 묻는 문장을 말한다.

1 부정의문문 만들기

의문문 제일 앞에 오는 be동사나 조동사 뒤에 not을 붙인다. 이때는 반드시 축약형을 쓴다.

ex. 의문문   **Do you go to school?**
너는 학교에 가니?

부정의문문   **Don't you go to school?**
너는 학교에 가지 않니?

~~Do not you go to school?~~

긍정으로 묻든 부정으로 묻든 관계 없이, 질문에 대한 대답이 긍정이면 Yes, ~ 부정이면 No, ~ 로 대답한다.

ex. **Don't you drink coffee?**   너 커피 마시지 않지?

   – **Yes, I do.** (I drink coffee.)   – **No, I don't.** (I don't drink coffee.)
     아니, 나는 마셔.   응, 나는 안마셔.

부가의문문이란?
우리말의 '그렇지?, 그렇지 않니?'하고, 동의를 구하거나 사실의 진위를 확인하기 위해 평서문 뒤에 붙이는 짧은 의문문을 말한다.

2 부가의문문 만들기

 앞의 문장이 긍정이면 부정의 의문문을, 앞의 문장이 부정이면 긍정의 의문문을 붙인다.
이때도, 반드시 축약형을 쓴다.

ex. <u>**She is a nurse,**</u> <u>**isn't she?**</u>   그녀는 간호사야, 그렇지 않니?
        긍정   부정

       <u>**She isn't a nurse,**</u> <u>**is she?**</u>   그녀는 간호사가 아니야, 그렇지?
          부정   긍정

대답은 부정의문문과 같다.

ex. **He is a teacher, isn't he?** 그는 선생님이야, 그렇지 않니?

 – **Yes, he is.** (He is a teacher.)　 – **No, he isn't.** (He isn't a teacher.)
　 응, 그래.　　　　　　　　　　　　 아니, 그렇지 않아.

2 부가의문문은 앞의 평서문과 동사의 종류 및 시제를 일치시킨다.

▶ 동사의 종류 일치

ex. **He has dinner, doesn't he?**　　 그는 저녁을 먹어, 그렇지 않니?
　　　 일반동사　　　　　 일반동사

 ❶ 앞의 문장을 먼저 의문문으로 고친다.
　 He has dinner.의 의문문은 **Does he have dinner?**

 ❷ 이를 부정이나 긍정으로 고쳐서 짧게 덧붙이는 부정의문문이나 의문문을 만들어 붙여주면 된다.

▶ 시제의 일치

ex. **They <u>study</u> English, <u>don't</u> they?**　　 그들은 영어 공부를 해, 그렇지 않니?
　　　　　 현재　　　　　　　 현재

　 They <u>studied</u> English, <u>didn't</u> they?　　 그들은 영어 공부를 했어, 그렇지 않니?
　　　　　 과거　　　　　　　 과거

　 They <u>will study</u> English, <u>won't</u> they?　 그들은 영어 공부를 할 거야, 그렇지 않니?
　　　　　 미래　　　　　　　　 미래

3 부가의문문에서는 앞 평서문의 명사를 대명사로 받는다.

ex. **Jane goes to library, doesn't she?**　 Jane은 도서관에 가, 그렇지 않니?

　 Jane은 3인칭 단수이므로 대명사 she로 받는다.

명령문 · 권유문의 부가의문문

명령문이나 권유문에 **will you?** 나 **shall we?**를 덧붙인다.

이는 명령문의 느낌을 좀 더 부드럽게 해 준다.

명령문	+ will you?
Let's로 시작하는 권유문	+ shall we?

ex. **Open the door, will you?**　　 문 좀 열지 않을래?
　 Let's go there, shall we?　 우리 거기 가지 않을래?

다음 문장의 시제와 동사를 고르고, 부정의문문으로 알맞은 말을 골라 보자.

bite 물다, 물어 뜯다
sweet potato 고구마
mirror 거울

1 He is a great artist. (현재), 과거, 미래) (be동사, 일반동사)

⇨ ((Isn't), Doesn't) he a great artist?

2 You bought me a schoolbag. (현재, 과거, 미래) (be동사, 일반동사)

⇨ (Doesn't, Didn't) you buy me a schoolbag?

3 The horse bites a sweet potato. (현재, 과거, 미래) (be동사, 일반동사)

⇨ (Doesn't, Didn't) the horse bite a sweet potato?

4 It tastes good. (현재, 과거, 미래) (be동사, 일반동사)

⇨ (Isn't, Doesn't) it taste good?

5 They will move to Paris. (현재, 과거, 미래) (be동사, 일반동사)

⇨ (Won't, Don't) they move to Paris?

6 Jane has a pair of long boots. (현재, 과거, 미래) (be동사, 일반동사)

⇨ (Isn't, Doesn't) Jane have a pair of long boots?

7 She broke a mirror. (현재, 과거, 미래) (be동사, 일반동사)

⇨ (Didn't, Doesn't) she break a mirror?

8 You are very hungry. (현재, 과거, 미래) (be동사, 일반동사)

⇨ (Isn't, Aren't) you very hungry?

9 Paul was at home. (현재, 과거, 미래) (be동사, 일반동사)

⇨ (Isn't, Wasn't) Paul at home?

10 You will go to church on Sundays. (현재, 과거, 미래) (be동사, 일반동사)

⇨ (Don't, Won't) you go to church on Sundays?

2

다음 ( ) 안의 우리말을 참고하여, 질문에 알맞은 대답을 골라 보자.

1 Doesn't it rain?

– (Yes, No), (it, they) (does, do). (비가 온다)

2 Wasn't Tom famous?

– (Yes, No), (she, he) (isn't, wasn't). (유명하지 않았다)

3 Didn't your mom travel in Asia?

– (Yes, No), (she, he) (does, did). (여행을 했다)

4 Don't you meet them?

– (Yes, No), (I, you) (don't, doesn't). (그들을 만나지 않는다)

5 Can't kangaroos jump high?

– (Yes, No), (it, they) (can, can't). (높이 점프할 수 있다)

6 Aren't there three airplanes in Gimpo Airport?

– (Yes, No), (they, there) (are, were). (비행기들이 있다)

7 Weren't you very sick yesterday?

– (Yes, No), (I, we) (was, wasn't). (아프지 않았다)

8 Didn't it snow?

– (Yes, No), (it, that) (don't, didn't). (눈이 오지 않았다)

9 Won't James feed a dog?

– (Yes, No), (it, he) (will, won't). (개에게 먹이를 줄 것이다)

10 Isn't it expensive?

– (Yes, No), (they, it) (is, isn't). (비싸지 않다)

---

take a trip 여행하다
kangaroo 캥거루
feed 먹이를 주다
expensive 값 비싼

Unit 08 161

다음 문장의 시제를 고르고 (   ) 안에서 알맞은 말을 골라 동그라미 해 보자.

scientist 과학자

1 You are a scientist, (aren't, are) you?　　　(현재, 과거, 미래)

You will be a scientist, (willn't, won't) you?　　　(현재, 과거, 미래)

You aren't a scientist, (are, aren't) you?　　　(현재, 과거, 미래)

You weren't a scientist, (were, weren't) you?　　　(현재, 과거, 미래)

2 Tom sleeps well, (doesn't, does) he?　　　(현재, 과거, 미래)

Tom slept well, (did, didn't) he?　　　(현재, 과거, 미래)

Tom doesn't sleep well, (does, did) he?　　　(현재, 과거, 미래)

Tom didn't sleep well, (does, did) he?　　　(현재, 과거, 미래)

3 Bring me some water, (will you, shall we)?　　　(명령문, 권유문)

He doesn't build his house, (did, does) he?　　　(현재, 과거, 미래)

He didn't build his house, (does, did) he?　　　(현재, 과거, 미래)

He builds his house, (isn't, doesn't) he?　　　(현재, 과거, 미래)

4 She doesn't forget it, (does, did) she?　　　(현재, 과거, 미래)

She forgot it, (didn't, did) she?　　　(현재, 과거, 미래)

She didn't forget it, (did, does) she?　　　(현재, 과거, 미래)

Let's join them, (will you, shall we)?　　　(명령문, 권유문)

4

다음 ( ) 안에서 알맞은 말을 골라 동그라미 해 보자.

1 He has many coins, (does, (doesn't)) ((he), she)?

Tom and Bill don't have many coins,

(do Tom and Bill, do they)?

They had many coins, (did they, didn't they)?

They didn't have many coins, (did they, do they)?

2 Maria is tired, (isn't Maria, isn't she)?

Maria isn't tired, (is she, was she)?

Maria was tired, (is Maria, wasn't she)?

Maria wasn't tired, (was she, wasn't she)?

3 You will visit him, (will you, won't you)?

You will not visit him, (will you, won't you)?

Let's walk to church, (shall we, will you)?

Walk to the museum, (shall we, will you)?

4 He and she were your cousins,

(weren't he and she, weren't they)?

He and she aren't your cousins, (are they, were they)?

He and she are your cousins, (are they, aren't they)?

He and she weren't your cousins,

(were he and she, were they)?

coin 동전
tired 피곤한, 지친
museum 박물관
cousin 사촌

3 명령문, will you?
권유문, shall we?

다음 빈칸에 알맞은 말을 써 넣어 부정의문문과 대답을 완성해 보자.

take cafe of ~을 돌보다
go camping 캠핑가다

1 *Isn't* Minsu small? (작다)

| | Yes | , | he | is | . |

2 Can't she take care of the baby? (돌볼 수 없다)

| | | , | | | . |

3 they go camping? (캠핑 갈 것이다)

| | Yes | , | they | will | . |

4 Aren't Tom and John famous writers? (유명한 작가들이다)

| | | , | | | . |

5 Mary silent? (조용하지 않았다)

| | No | , | she | wasn't | . |

6 the boy write his name? (쓸 수 있다)

| | Yes | , | he | can | . |

7 Doesn't he drink coffee everday? (매일 마시지 않는다)

| | | , | | | . |

8 you want to be a model? (모델 되기를 원치 않는다)

| | No | , | I | don't | . |

9 Won't Jane stay in L.A? (L.A에 머무를 것이다)

| | | , | | | . |

10 you lazy? (게으르지 않다)

| | No | , | I'm | not | . |

2

다음 빈칸에 알맞은 말을 써 넣어 부가의문문을 완성해 보자.

1 My mom has a pretty necklace,   *doesn't*   *she*   ?

2 This textbook isn't yours,   ?

3 Let's take a shower,   ?

4 He was rich,   ?

5 John doesn't have a donkey,   ?

6 You weren't a celebrity then,   ?

7 She will be at home,   ?

8 My parents didn't go hiking,   ?

9 Her brother put it on the desk,   ?

10 She doesn't have breakfast,   ?

11 All children don't want to go to hospital,

              ?

12 Do it quickly,   ?

13 She doesn't remember the sentence,

              ?

14 He can raise many pigs,   ?

15 You are not sad,   ?

textbook 교과서
donkey 당나귀
celebrity 연예인
quickly 빠르게
sentence 문장
raise pigs 돼지를 치다

다음 빈칸에 알맞은 말을 써 넣어 부가의문문을 완성해 보자.

clothes 옷
department store 백화점
lawyer 변호사
be proud of ~를 자랑스러워하다
trust 신뢰하다
thief 도둑
by Monday 월요일까지

1 Your sister has a lot of clothes, *doesn't* *she* ?

2 Let's go to the department store together, _____ _____ ?

3 Pass me the salt, _____ _____ ?

4 They were not from Canada, _____ _____ ?

5 We are always proud of our family, _____ _____ ?

6 You don't trust me, _____ _____ ?

7 Amy will go to the summer camp, _____ _____ ?

8 The policemen caught the thief, _____ _____ ?

9 Turn off the TV and all the lights, _____ _____ ?

10 You eat carrots, _____ _____ ?

11 Mr. Brown isn't an excellent golfer, _____ _____ ?

12 Sara doesn't leave for London today, _____ _____ ?

13 Miss Lee was your mother's best friend, _____ _____ ?

14 You were in the dining room, _____ _____ ?

15 He can finish this work by Monday, _____ _____ ?

4

다음 빈칸에 알맞은 말을 써 넣어 부가의문문과 대답을 완성해 보자.

1 You don't have much money, **do** **you** ?

  No , **I** **don't** . (많은 돈을 가지고 있지 않다)

2 Close the door for me, ⬚ ⬚ ?

3 You will buy me this skirt, ⬚ ⬚ ?

  ⬚ , ⬚ ⬚ . (이 치마를 사주지 않을 것이다)

4 She is a new student from Japan, ⬚ ⬚ ?

  ⬚ , ⬚ . (일본에서 온 새로운 학생이다)

5 The fire fighter saved my son, ⬚ ⬚ ?

  ⬚ , ⬚ . (내 아들을 구했다)

6 Let's go to see the fireworks, ⬚ ⬚ ?

7 They aren't coming with us, ⬚ ⬚ ?

  ⬚ , ⬚ ⬚ . (우리와 함께 오고 있다)

8 Mr. Bush can drive a car in Seoul, ⬚ ⬚ ?

  ⬚ , ⬚ ⬚ . (서울에서 차를 운전할 수 있다)

9 Tommy didn't cry, ⬚ ⬚ ?

  ⬚ , ⬚ ⬚ . (울지 않았다)

10 She picks him up at the airport. ⬚ ⬚ ?

  ⬚ , ⬚ ⬚ . (공항에서 그를 픽업한다)

---

actress 여배우
save 구조하다
fireworks 불꽃놀이
pick ~up ~를 차에 태우다

다음 밑줄 친 부분을 바르게 고쳐 써 보자.

refrigerator 냉장고
husband 남편
plaza 광장
engineer 기술자; 공학자

1 They cross the street, <u>aren't they</u>?
don't they

2 Let's carry the refrigerator, <u>will you</u>?

3 She didn't love her husband, <u>didn't she</u>?

4 Linda and Mary were good friends, <u>don't they</u>?

5 He didn't become a great musician, <u>does he</u>?

6 Look at this tulip, <u>shall we</u>?

7 She shows me her uniform, <u>does she</u>?

8 Judy learned history, <u>didn't Judy</u>?

9 There are many buses in the plaza, <u>are there</u>?

10 Try it, <u>shall we</u>?

11 They are my cousins, <u>weren't they</u>?

12 Mary had lunch, <u>hadn't she</u>?

13 He isn't at home, <u>was he</u>?

14 You are an engineer, <u>don't you</u>?

15 Tom and Judy are angry, <u>aren't Tom and Judy</u>?

2

다음 밑줄 친 부분을 바르게 고쳐 써 보자.

mistake 실수
score 점수
set the alarm clock 알람을
맞추어 놓다

1 Babies smile a lot, <u>do they</u>?
don't they

2 He will make me happy, <u>wasn't he</u>?

3 Take my hand, <u>won't you</u>?

4 They ran to the store, <u>do they</u>?

5 Let's help the old man, <u>will we</u>?

6 You didn't make many mistakes, <u>didn't you</u>?

7 Mina had the best score in our class, <u>was she</u>?

8 Your best friend lives in Hawaii, <u>did she</u>?

9 There are a few plastic forks on the table, <u>weren't there</u>?

10 My father had three houses in America, <u>did he</u>?

11 My students are kind and diligent, <u>aren't my students</u>?

12 Set the alarm clock for me, <u>do you</u>?

13 You have a good time with your friends, <u>didn't you</u>?

14 My cousins came to our house yesterday, <u>weren't you</u>?

15 Let's have some hamburgers and French fries, <u>don't we</u>?

더알아보기

01 다음 대화의 빈칸에 공통으로 들어갈 말로 알맞은 것은? (대소문자 무시)

> A : I think Mary is very kind. _____ you think so?
>
> B : No, I _____.

① do
② don't
③ does
④ doesn't
⑤ aren't

02 다음 대화의 빈칸에 들어갈 말로 알맞은 것은?

> A : Didn't you call me yesterday?
>
> B : _____
>
> I didn't have your phone number then.

① Yes, I did.
② Yes, I didn't.
③ No, I did.
④ No, I didn't.
⑤ No, I don't.

03 다음 대화에서 <u>틀린</u> 부분을 바르게 고쳐 쓰시오.

> A : Don't you know Sandy?
>
> B : Yes, I did. I know her.

_____ ⇨ _____

04 다음 문장을 부정의문문으로 바꿀 때, 올바른 것은?

> My daughter draws her face with a pencil.

① Isn't my daughter draws her face with a pencil?
② Isn't my daughter draw her face with a pencil?
③ Don't my daughter draws her face with a pencil?
④ Doesn't my daughter draw her face with a pencil?
⑤ Doesn't my daughter draws her face with a pencil?

05 다음 문장의 주어를 my father 로 바꿀 때, 빈칸에 알맞은 것은?

> Aren't you angry?
>
> → _____ my father angry?

① Don't   ② Doesn't
③ Isn't   ④ Wasn't
⑤ Weren't

06 다음 문장 중 바르지 <u>않은</u> 것은?

① He doesn't love Judy, does he?
② She was interested in math, wasn't she?
③ You will be there, won't you?
④ You can cook the chicken, can't you?
⑤ My sister were sick, were they?

[07–08] 다음 빈칸에 알맞은 부가의문문을 고르시오.

07

| My uncle went to his office, _____? |

① is he
② doesn't he
③ didn't he
④ isn't he
⑤ didn't my uncle

08

| Jenny is not American, _____? |

① does she
② is Jenny
③ isn't Jenny
④ isn't she
⑤ is she

09 다음을 부가의문문이 되도록 할 때, 빈칸에 알맞은 말을 |보기|에서 고르시오.

|보기| ⓐ will you   ⓑ won't you   ⓒ shall we

(A) Let's open the box, _____ ?

(B) Look at the picture, _____ !

10 다음 문장에서 <u>틀린</u> 부분을 바르게 고쳐 쓰시오.

Bill has a cellphone, doesn't Bill?

_____ ⇨ _____

Quiz!

다음 빈칸에 알맞은 말을 써 넣어 부가의문문을 완성해 보자.

1　He drinks some coffee, ＿＿＿ ＿＿＿ ?

2　You were sad yesterday, ＿＿＿ ＿＿＿ ?

3　The young men can walk fast, ＿＿＿ ＿＿＿ ?

4　She doesn't repeat the words, ＿＿＿ ＿＿＿ ?

5　Do the exercise every day, ＿＿＿ ＿＿＿ ?

6　Judy is angry, ＿＿＿ ＿＿＿ ?

7　Mr. Kim cut the pine tree, ＿＿＿ ＿＿＿ ?

8　My brother won't be a painter, ＿＿＿ ＿＿＿ ?

9　They can't sleep well, ＿＿＿ ＿＿＿ ?

10　John ordered spaghetti, ＿＿＿ ＿＿＿ ?

11　Let's watch TV, ＿＿＿ ＿＿＿ ?

12　She was beautiful, ＿＿＿ ＿＿＿ ?

13　He isn't at the front door, ＿＿＿ ＿＿＿ ?

14　He will take some medicine, ＿＿＿ ＿＿＿ ?

15　I didn't go on a picnic with Mary, ＿＿＿ ＿＿＿ ?

- **Review Test 2**
- **내신대비 2**

01 다음 ( ) 안에서 알맞은 동사를 골라 과거진행형을 만들어 보자.

1 She (was, were) (reads, reading) a book.

2 I (was, were) (slept, sleeping) in the room.

3 We (was, were) (played, playing) tennis.

4 Tom (was, were) (studying, studied) English.

5 They (was, were) (swiming, swimming) in a pool.

02 우리말에 알맞게 빈칸을 채워 보자.

1 ☐ ☐ ☐ his homework.
그는 숙제를 하고 있는 중이었다.

2 ☐ ☐ ☐ at the market. shop 쇼핑하다
엄마는 마켓에서 쇼핑을 하고 있는 중이었다.

3 ☐ ☐ ☐ to school.
우리는 학교에 가고 있는 중이었다.

4 ☐ ☐ ☐ his car.
나의 삼촌은 그의 차를 닦고 있는 중이었다.

5 ☐ ☐ ☐ up the house. clean up 청소하다
그들은 집을 청소하고 있는 중이었다.

03 다음 문장을 지시대로 바꾸고 의문문은 대답도 완성해 보자.

1 He was doing the dishes.

부정문 ☐ ☐ ☐ the dishes.

2 She was brushing her hair.

의문문 ☐ ☐ her hair?   Yes, ☐ ☐ .

3 We were watching a movie.

부정문 ☐ ☐ a movie.

4 They were taking a walk.

의문문 ☐ ☐ ☐ a walk?   Yes, ☐ ☐ .

5 I was going to the post office.

부정문 ☐ ☐ to the post office.

6 Dad was reading the newspaper.

의문문 ☐ ☐ ☐ the newspaper?

No, ☐ ☐ .

7 It was snowing in Seoul.

부정문 ☐ ☐ in Seoul.

8 The dog was eating food.

의문문 ☐ ☐ food?   No, ☐ ☐ .

9 We were working together.

부정문 ☐ ☐ together.

10 Sumi was writing a diary.

의문문 ☐ ☐ ☐ a diary?

Yes, ☐ ☐ .

O1 다음 (   ) 안에서 알맞은 동사를 골라 미래형을 만들어 보자.

1 He (is, will) (buys, buy) the book.

2 Jane (is, will) going to (visit, visiting) him.

3 They (are, will) going to (build, built) a bridge.

4 We (are, will) (make, making) a snowman.

5 I (am, will) (be, is) a lawyer.

O2 다음 두 문장의 뜻이 같도록 빈칸에 알맞은 말을 써 보자.

1 We will have lunch together.

= We _____ _____ _____ lunch together.

2 I will take a bus.

= I _____ _____ _____ a bus.

3 She is going to watch a movie.

= She _____ _____ a movie.

4 Jake will ride a bike.

= Jake _____ _____ _____ a bike.

5 Tom and I are going to learn Chinese.

= Tom and I _____ _____ Chinese.

03 다음 문장을 지시대로 바꾸고 의문문은 대답도 완성해 보자.

1 He will come back to Italy.

부정문   back to Italy.

2 She will make lunch.

의문문   lunch?   Yes,   .

3 He is going to walk to school.

부정문   to school.

4 They are going to swim in a pool.

의문문   in a pool?

                                         Yes,   .

5 I will be a doctor.

부정문   a doctor.

6 Jane is going to clean her room.

의문문   her room?

                               No,   .

7 It will rain this weekend.

부정문   this weekend.

8 Tom will play PC games.

의문문   PC games?   No,   .

9 We are going to sing together.

부정문   together.

10 You are going to be an engineer.

의문문   an engineer?

                                   Yes,   .

01 다음 (   ) 안에서 알맞은 감탄사를 골라 보자.

1　(How, What) smart the boy is!

2　(How, What) a nice shirt it is!

3　(How, What) cold it is!

4　(How, What) an excellent idea you have!

5　(How, What) big watermelons these are!

6　(How, What) expensive these are!

7　(How, What) big eyes the doll has!

02 다음 (   ) 안의 단어를 바르게 배열하여 감탄문을 만들어 보자.

1　(the, is, pretty, baby, how)!

⇨ _____ !

2　(he, king, a, is, what, wise)!

⇨ _____ !

3　(how, tunnel, the, is, long)!

⇨ _____ !

4　(what, it, an, is, story, interesting)!

⇨ _____ !

5　(these, trees, are, what, tall)!

⇨ _____ !

03 다음 문장을 감탄문으로 바꿔 쓸 때, 빈칸을 알맞은 말로 채워 보자.

1 He walks very fast.

⇨ ▭ ▭ he walks!

2 This is a very thick book. thick 두꺼운

⇨ ▭ ▭ ▭ ▭ this is!

3 The tall mountains are very great.

⇨ ▭ ▭ the tall mountains are!

4 It was a very exciting game.

⇨ ▭ ▭ ▭ it was!

5 These are very difficult problems.

⇨ ▭ ▭ these are!

04 다음 문장을 감탄문으로 바꿔 보자.

1 The movie is very boring.

⇨ ▭ !

2 This is a very deep lake.

⇨ ▭ !

3 They are very brave fire-fighters.

⇨ ▭ !

4 The puppies are very small.

⇨ ▭ !

5 She is a very important person.

⇨ ▭ !

01   다음은 부정의문문이다. (　) 안에서 알맞은 말을 골라 동그라미 해 보자.

1   (Aren't, Don't) you like swimming?   I like swimming.   (Yes, No) ~.

2   (Wasn't, Didn't) he lazy?   He wasn't lazy.   (Yes, No) ~.

3   (Isn't, Doesn't) mom upset?   She isn't upset.   (Yes, No) ~.

4   (Weren't, Didn't) they keep a pet?   They kept a pet.   (Yes, No) ~.

5   (Isn't, Doesn't) it raining there?   It is raining.   (Yes, No) ~.

6   (Aren't, Don't) you have money?   I have money.   (Yes, No) ~.

7   (Wasn't, Didn't) there anything in the box?

        There aren't anything in the box.   (Yes, No) ~.

02   다음 (　) 안에서 알맞은 말을 골라 동그라미 해 보자.

1   He is a vet, (is, isn't) he?   vet 수의사

2   You aren't busy, (are, aren't) you?

3   She was sick, (was, wasn't) she?

4   Tom finished his homework, (doesn't, didn't) he?

5   They didn't go to the park, (did, didn't) they?

6   Go straight, (don't, will) (you, we)?

7   Let's meet on Saturday, (shall, will) (you, we)?

03 다음 빈칸에 알맞은 말을 써 넣어 부정의문문을 완성해 보고 대답도 써 보자.

1 She is a new teacher.

⇨ ＿＿＿＿ ＿＿＿＿ a new teacher?　　Yes, ＿＿＿＿ ＿＿＿＿ .

2 You(너는) know the fact.

⇨ ＿＿＿＿ ＿＿＿＿ ＿＿＿＿ the fact?　　No, ＿＿＿＿ ＿＿＿＿ .

3 It was very cold last winter.

⇨ ＿＿＿＿ ＿＿＿＿ very cold last winter?　　Yes, ＿＿＿＿ ＿＿＿＿ .

4 They were at school.

⇨ ＿＿＿＿ ＿＿＿＿ at school?　　No, ＿＿＿＿ ＿＿＿＿ .

5 Tom heard the news.

⇨ ＿＿＿＿ ＿＿＿＿ ＿＿＿＿ the news?　　Yes, ＿＿＿＿ ＿＿＿＿ .

04 다음 빈칸에 알맞은 말을 써 넣어 부가의문문을 완성해 보고 대답도 써 보자.

1 Tom is honest, ＿＿＿＿ ＿＿＿＿ ?　　Yes, ＿＿＿＿ ＿＿＿＿ .

2 Jane has a sister, ＿＿＿＿ ＿＿＿＿ ?　　No, ＿＿＿＿ ＿＿＿＿ .

3 He will be a pilot, ＿＿＿＿ ＿＿＿＿ ?　　Yes, ＿＿＿＿ ＿＿＿＿ .

4 She wasn't at home, ＿＿＿＿ ＿＿＿＿ ?　　Yes, ＿＿＿＿ ＿＿＿＿ .

5 You(너는) didn't have lunch, ＿＿＿＿ ＿＿＿＿ ?　　No, ＿＿＿＿ ＿＿＿＿ .

6 There is something it, ＿＿＿＿ ＿＿＿＿ ?　　Yes, ＿＿＿＿ ＿＿＿＿ .

7 It doesn't smell bad, ＿＿＿＿ ＿＿＿＿ ?　　No, ＿＿＿＿ ＿＿＿＿ .

01 다음 우리말을 영어로 쓸 때, 빈칸에 알맞은 말은?

> Tom의 부모님은 거실에서 TV를 보고 있는 중이었다.
>
> → Tom's parents _____ TV in the livingroom.

① was watching
② were watching
③ is watching
④ are watching
⑤ am watching

02 다음 문장 중 옳지 <u>않은</u> 것을 고르면?

① She wasn't going to school.
② We were playing soccer.
③ I were walking my dog.
④ He wasn't driving a car.
⑤ They were talking to each other.

03 다음 빈칸에 들어갈 말로 알맞은 것은?

> Jane was playing the cello
> _____

① tomorrow morning
② tomorrow
③ next year
④ now
⑤ then

04 다음 질문에 대한 대답으로 알맞은 것은?

> A : Were they helping mom?
> B : _____

① No, they weren't.
② Yes, they are.
③ Yes, they did.
④ No, they aren't.
⑤ Yes, they didn't

05 주어진 문장을 부정문으로 바꿔 보시오.

> Mom was driving a car.

⇨ _____

06 다음을 과거진행형으로 바꿔 보시오.

Bill and I study in the library.

→ Bill and I _____

_____.

07 다음에서 어법상 <u>틀린</u> 문장은?

① Tom will go to the meeting.
② They will have dinner together.
③ I will be a scientist.
④ She will does the dishes.
⑤ We will play soccer.

08 다음 빈칸에 알맞은 말은?

Jane _____ wear a skirt
tomorrow.

① don't
② isn't
③ didn't
④ wasn't
⑤ won't

09 다음 빈칸에 들어갈 말로 알맞지 <u>않은</u> 것은?

I will visit my grandmother
_____.

① on Saturday
② next week
③ this weekend
④ last Sunday
⑤ tomorrow

10 다음 대화의 빈칸에 들어갈 말로 알맞은 것은?

A : Where are you going to stay
tonight?
B : I _____ stay at my
uncle's.

① am going to
② will going to
③ am go to
④ will going
⑤ do going to

11 다음 문장 중 옳은 것은?

① She is going not to invite Bill.
② Does he going to send a message?
③ He is not going to keeps a dog.
④ Are they going to close the store?
⑤ I am going to will see a movie.

12 다음 빈칸에 알맞은 말은?

> · Will you go shopping?
> · No, I _____ .

① am not
② don't
③ won't
④ didn't
⑤ wasn't

13 다음 두 문장의 뜻이 같도록 빈칸에 알맞은 말을 써 보시오.

> Susan will not play the piano today.
> = Susan _____ _____
> _____ _____ the piano today.

14 다음 질문에 대한 대답으로 옳은 것 두 개를 고르면?

> Will you help your mom?

① Yes, you will.
② Yes, I will.
③ No, you will not.
④ No, you won't.
⑤ No, I won't.

5 다음 빈칸에 들어갈 말이 순서대로 바르게 짝 지어진 것은?

> · _____ busy I am!
> · _____ big ships they are!

① How - What
② How - How
③ What - How
④ What - What
⑤ Who - How

6 다음 빈칸에 들어갈 말로 알맞지 <u>않은</u> 것은?

> What a smart _____ he is!

① students
② boy
③ man
④ child
⑤ kid

7 다음 단어들을 배열하여 감탄문으로 만들어 보시오.

> book, thick, is, this, how
>
> → _____
>
> _____

18 다음에서 어법상 <u>틀린</u> 것은?

① How diligent the boy is!
② What a cold day it is!
③ What brave soldiers they are!
④ What an interesting story they are!
⑤ How delicious these cookies are!

19 다음 문장의 빈칸에 올 수 있는 말을 |보기|에서 고르시오.

> | 보기 | ⓐ the boy is   ⓑ is the boy

(A) How tall _____ ?

(B) How tall _____ !

20 다음 문장을 감탄문으로 바꿔 보시오.

> It is a very exciting game.
>
> → _____
>
> _____

21 다음 문장을 부정의문문으로 바꿀 때, 빈칸에 올바른 것은?

> Tom saw the movie.
> → _____ the movie?

① Wasn't Tom see
② Wasn't Tom saw
③ Don't Tom saw
④ Didn't Tom see
⑤ Doesn't Tom see

22 다음 빈칸에 알맞은 부가의문문은?

> His grandfather was a great artist, _____ ?

① was he
② doesn't he
③ didn't he
④ wasn't he
⑤ didn't my uncle

23 다음 질문에 대한 대답으로 옳은 것은?

> Doesn't he go out at night?

① Yes, he go.
② Yes, he doesn't.
③ No, he isn't.
④ No, he doesn't
⑤ Yes, he is.

24 다음은 부정의문문이다. 밑줄친 곳을 바르게 고쳐 보시오.

> <u>Doesn't</u> they work with Billy?

_____ ⇨ _____

25 다음 빈칸에 알맞은 대답을 써 보시오.

> Didn't she wear a cap?
> Yes, _____

1·2회

종합문제

01 다음 중 서수의 표기가 바르지 <u>않은</u> 것은?

① 9th : ninth
② 5th : fiveth
③ 2nd : second
④ 11th : eleventh
⑤ 100th : one hundredth

02 다음 빈칸에 공통으로 들어갈 말로 가장 알맞은 것은?

· I must finish this work

_____. (우선 이일을 끝내야 한다.)

· Wow! The _____ snow of

this year! (와! 올해 첫눈이다!)

① one
② second
③ first
④ third
⑤ a

03 다음 중 「2006년 4월 5일」을 바르게 쓴 것은?

① 2006, April 5th
② 2006, 5th April
③ 5th April, 2006
④ April 5th, 2006
⑤ April, 2006, 5th

04 다음 분수를 읽은 것 중 바르지 <u>않은</u> 것은?

① $\frac{1}{4}$: a fourth
② $\frac{1}{5}$: one-fifth
③ $\frac{2}{6}$: two sixths
④ $\frac{4}{7}$: four-sevenths
⑤ $\frac{1}{8}$: one-eight

05 다음 전화번호를 바르게 읽어 보시오.

401-2325

⇨ _____

06 다음 빈칸에 들어갈 말로 알맞은 것은?

_____ is cloudy.

① This
② That
③ It
④ These
⑤ Those

07 다음 글에서 밑줄 친 시각을 바르게 읽은 것은? (2개)

> It is John's birthday. Tonight we have a party. I will meet Ann and Roy at <u>9:30</u> and we will go to John's house together.

① half after nine
② half past nine
③ a half past nine
④ nine thirty
⑤ half to ten

08 다음 주어진 시각을 영어로 나타낼 때, 빈칸에 알맞은 말을 쓰시오.

> 4시 10분 전 - ten _____ four

09 다음 질문에 대한 대답을 바르게 짝지은 것은?

> (A) Do you have time?
> (B) Do you have the time?

> ⓐ It's 2 o'clock. ⓑ Yes, I do.

① (A) - ⓐ, (B) - ⓑ
② (A) - ⓐ, (B) - ⓐ
③ (A) - ⓑ, (B) - ⓐ
④ (A) - ⓑ, (B) - ⓑ
⑤ (A) - ⓐ, ⓑ, (B) - ⓐ, ⓑ

10 다음 중 시각을 바르게 읽은 것은?

① 3시 5분 전 - It's five past three.
② 4시 14분 - It's fourteen to four.
③ 8시 15분 전 - It's a quarter to eight.
④ 10시 20분 - It's twenty to ten.
⑤ 9시 15분 - It's fifteen nine.

11 다음 중 동사의 현재형과 과거형이 바르게 연결되지 <u>않은</u> 것은?

① am - was
② study - studied
③ see - saw
④ make - made
⑤ stop - stoped

12 다음 중 어법상 옳은 것은?

① He was taking care of his baby.
② I were watering the flower pot.
③ She was make a doll.
④ They was talking with their teacher.
⑤ We was skiing then.

13 주어진 문장을 부정문으로 바꿔 보시오.

They were having fun.

⇨ _____

14 주어진 질문에 알맞은 대답은?

Were the boys standing at the bus stop?

① Yes, they are.
② Yes, they do.
③ Yes, they weren't.
④ No, they aren't.
⑤ No, they weren't.

15 다음 빈칸에 들어갈 말로 알맞은 것은?

· He _____ searching on the internet.
· I _____ surfing on the internet.

① does - are
② is - do
③ was - were
④ was - was
⑤ was - are

search 찾다 surf 검색하다

16 우리말에 알맞은 것을 고르시오.

Tom _____ his homework after school.
Tom은 방과 후에 그의 숙제를 하고 있었다.
Tom _____ his homework after school.
Tom은 방과 후에 그의 숙제를 했다.

① is doing - did
② was doing - does
③ is doing - did
④ was doing - did
⑤ was doing - do

[7–18] 다음 글을 읽고 질문에 답하시오.

> Jack and Amy _____
> shopping together. They
> went to the ABC market. Jack
> needed a toy for his son and
> Amy wanted to buy some fruit.
> There _____ so many people
> in the market. There were many
> things, too. Jack bought a robot.
> Amy bought a bunch of bananas
> and five melons.
> It _____ good shopping.

7 위 글의 빈칸에 들어갈 말이 순서대로 바르게
짝지어진 것은?

① go - were - am
② go - were - was
③ went - were - was
④ went - were - were
⑤ went - was - were

18 위 글의 내용과 일치하지 <u>않는</u> 것은?

① Jack과 Amy는 쇼핑을 했다.
② Jack은 딸에게 줄 인형을 원했다.
③ Amy는 과일을 사기를 원했다.
④ 시장에는 사람들이 많이 있었다.
⑤ Amy는 바나나 한 다발과 멜론 5개를 샀다.

19 다음 밑줄 친 부분 중 바르지 <u>않은</u> 것은?

① I <u>were</u> very tired.
② You <u>were</u> a handsome boy.
③ Mina <u>was</u> happy.
④ We <u>were</u> good teachers then.
⑤ They <u>were</u> my friends.

20 다음 문장을 과거형으로 바르게 바꿔 쓴 것은?

> He cuts the big tree.

① He cut the big tree.
② He cuted the big tree.
③ He cutted the big tree.
④ He had cut the big tree.
⑤ He did cut the big tree.

01 다음 문장을 부정문으로 만들 때, not이 들어 갈 위치로 알맞은 곳은?

> He ① was ② very ③ sick
> ④ yesterday ⑤ .

02 다음 문장을 의문문으로 바꿀 때, 올바른 것은?

> Your brother watched TV last night.

① Does your brother watched TV last night?

② Did your brother watches TV last night?

③ Did your brother watched TV last night?

④ Did your brother watch TV last night?

⑤ Your brother did watch TV last night?

03 다음 질문에 대한 대답이 바르게 짝지어진 것은? (2개)

> (A) Were they in the library?
> (B) Did they read the books?

> ⓐ Yes, they were.
> ⓑ Yes, they did.

① (A) - ⓐ

② (A) - ⓑ

③ (B) - ⓐ

④ (B) - ⓑ

⑤ 답 없음

04 다음 문장을 부정문으로 만들 때, 빈칸에 들어갈 말로 알맞은 것은?

> My sister got up at six.
> → My sister didn't _____ up at six.

① get

② got

③ gets

④ getting

⑤ is getting

5 다음 문장에서 **틀린** 부분을 바르게 고쳐 쓰시오.

> Were the doctor busy?
> – Yes, he was.

_____ ⇨ _____

6 다음 두 문장이 같은 의미가 되도록 빈칸에 알맞은 말을 쓰시오.

> They will write letters.
> = They _____ write letters.

7 다음 문장을 부정문으로 바꿔 쓰시오.

> I will carry the luggage.
> → _____

luggage 수하물

8 다음 문장 중 바른 것은?

① He is going to calls me.
② She is going to sleeps now.
③ We are going to are good friends.
④ My brother is going to goes home.
⑤ Mary is going to take a bus.

09 다음 질문에 대한 대답으로 알맞은 것은? (2개)

> Will you take a bus?

① Yes, I am.
② Yes, I do.
③ No, I didn't.
④ Yes, I will.
⑤ No, I will not.

[10–11] 다음 문장 중 **틀린** 것을 고르시오.

10 ① I'm going to buy some books tomorrow.
② Jane is going to sell her car.
③ He will be at home at 8.
④ Mary is going to be 18 years old.
⑤ I am not going to work tomorrow.

11 ① She can speak English, can't she?
② He is drawing a picture, isn't he?
③ The woman will go to the party tonight, won't she?
④ Let's go on a picnic, shall we?
⑤ Tom didn't buy a cap, did Tom?

12 다음 중 빈칸에 들어갈 말이 <u>다른</u> 것은?

① _____ a famous writer Mary is!
② _____ a cute baby he is!
③ _____ wonderful the movie is!
④ _____ big monkeys they are!
⑤ _____ wise boys they are!

13 다음 빈칸에 공통으로 들어갈 말로 알맞은 것은?

> · _____ long is your hair?
> · _____ brave Kevin is!

① What
② When
③ Where
④ How
⑤ Be

14 다음 단어들을 바르게 배열하여 감탄문을 쓰시오.

> (an, watch, this, what, old, is, !)
> → _____

15 다음 문장에서 바르지 <u>않은</u> 부분 한 곳을 고르면?

> What sweet candy these are!

① What
② sweet
③ candy
④ these
⑤ are

16 주어진 문장을 감탄문으로 바꿔 쓰시오.

> My wife is very beautiful.
> → _____

17 다음 대화에서 바르지 <u>않은</u> 것은?

> A : She ① had a piano,
>   ② didn't ③ she?
> B : Yes, ④ she ⑤ does.

18 다음 문장을 부정의문문으로 바꿔 쓸 때, 빈칸에 들어갈 말이 순서대로 바르게 짝지어 진 것은?

> The horse runs fast.
> → _____ the horse _____ fast?

① Isn't - runs
② Aren't - run
③ Didn't - run
④ Doesn't - run
⑤ Don't - runs

19 주어진 우리말과 뜻이 같도록 빈칸에 알맞은 말을 쓰시오.

> A : Excuse me. You are a
>   policeman, aren't you?
> B : _____ , _____ _____.
>   (네, 그렇습니다.)
>   What's the problem?
> A : There is a thief over there.

20 다음 중 문장 뒤에 isn't he?의 부가의문문을 덧붙일 수 있는 것은?

① He plays soccer.
② He is a soccer player.
③ He played soccer.
④ He isn't playing soccer.
⑤ He will play soccer.

MEMO

정답 및 해설

Grammar
joy
4

이종저

POLY BOOKS

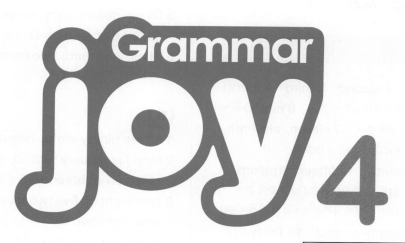

Grammar joy 4

정답 및 해설

POLY BOOKS

o1 기수, 서수

① **1** one, first   **2** second   **3** third   **4** fourth
5 fifth ▶five는 ve를 f로 바꾸고 th를 붙인다.   **6** ninth ▶nine의 마지막 e는 생략하고 th를 붙여 준다.   **7** eleven, eleventh
8 twelve, twelfth ▶ve를 f로 바꾸고 th를 붙여 준다.
9 fourteen, fourteenth   **10** fifteen, fifteenth
11 twenty/twentieth ▶y를 ie로 바꾸고 th를 붙여 준다.
12 twenty-first ▶21부터는 일의 자리만 서수로 바꿔 주면 된다.
13 twenty-two, twenty-second   **14** thirty, thirtieth **15** thirty-third

② **1** forty, fortieth   **2** forty-fourth   **3** forty-five, forty-fifth   **4** fifty, fiftieth   **5** fifty-first   **6** fifty-four, fifty-fourth   **7** fifty-fifth
8 sixtieth   **9** sixty-ninth   **10** seventieth
11 seventy-second   **12** eighty, eightieth
13 eighty-eight, eighty-eighth   **14** ninety, ninetieth   **15** one hundred, one hundredth

③ **1** tenth / ten   **2** sixth / six   **3** four / fourth
4 three / third   **5** two / second   **6** thirty / thirtieth   **7** fifth / five   **8** one / first

④ **1** ninth   **2** first   **3** two   **4** sixth
5 eighteen   **6** seventh   **7** eighth   **8** five
9 eight   **10** two   **11** four   **12** sixth   **13** twelve
14 two   **15** fifth

⑤
1 two thousand thirteen, eighteen fifty-one
▶연도는 두 자리씩 끊어 읽는다.
2 June eighteen, Thursday August eight nineteen forty-five
3 zero six four seven eight one five- ▶0이 앞에 올 때는 zero로 읽는다. one five four four one two oh five-

4 forty-five point six two, ninety-six point three nine
5 fifteen dollars eighty-two cents, ninety-six dollars eighteen cents
6 a half, one third, two thirds, one quarter ▶분자가 2이상이면 분모에 s를 붙여 준다.

⑥
1 fifteen ninety-eight, twenty eleven
2 Monday January second, Tuesday March fifth, nineteen eighteen ▶작은 단위부터 읽는다.
3 zero eight oh five two four two, zero four three nine eight two six
4 seventy-four point eight-nine, fifty-six point oh three
5 twenty-six dollars ninety three cents, fifty-eight dollars twelve cents
6 three quarters, three fifths
7 three and four-fifths, two and five-sevenths

① **1** the sixth   **2** the first ▶나는 1학년이다.
3 nineteen   **4** ten   **5** the second   **6** seven
7 the fifth ▶나의 사무실은 5층에 있다.   **8** three   **9** the ninth ▶그들은 9번째 문을 통과한다.   **10** one   **11** The first
12 four   **13** ten   **14** The seventh ▶9월의 일곱 번째 날은 나의 생일이다.   **15** eight

② **1** eleven   **2** the second ▶두 번째 단추를 눌러라!
3 two   **4** The third   **5** twelve ▶cow에 s가 붙어 복수형이므로 '농장에 12 마리의 소가 있다'는 뜻이다.   **6** ten   **7** The sixth
8 the fifteenth   **9** ten   **10** the twenty-fifth
11 nine   **12** fifth ▶다섯 번째 독후감.   **13** seven
14 the second ▶이것은 두 번째 시험이다.   **15** four

③ **1** sixth ▶분수의 분자는 기수로, 분모는 서수로 읽는다.
2 fifty ▶연도는 두 자리씩 읽는다.   **3** two thousand (=twenty)   **4** (and) twenty five cents   **5**

sixteen (sixteenth)   6 point one five   7 fourths (quarters)   8 two / three fourths (quarters)   9 -five three oh one   10 Monday / seven (seventh) ▶요일, 월, 일, 연도의 순으로 읽는다.   11 dollars   12 forty-six   13 the fifteenth   14 fifths   15 September twenty-two (second)

4   1 point seven five   2 dollars / cents   3 the twenty-seventh   4 eighth   5 zero   6 twenty-three   7 five (fifth) nineteen ninety-three   8 eighteen point   9 sevenths   10 one / oh / eight   11 seventy-two / six two   12 and   13 Friday / four (fourth)   14 (and) twenty-eight cents   15 five

실력쑥쑥   p.24~25

1   1 five → the fifth   2 nine five → ninety five ▶연도는 두 자리씩 끊어 읽는다.   3 forth → fourth(quarter)   4 seventeen → one seven ▶소수점 이하의 수는 한 자리씩 기수로 읽어 준다.   5 second → two   6 two → the second ▶병원 옆 두 번째 빌딩   7 oh → zero ▶제일 앞번호 '0'은 zero로 읽어 준다.   8 thirteen → thirteenth ▶13번째 생일, 즉 순서를 나타내므로 서수인 thirteenth가 되어야 한다.   9 seventy four fifteen → seven four one five ▶전화번호는 한 자리씩 읽어 준다.   10 two → half 11 thirtieth → thirty   12 cent → cents   13 three → third   14 fifth → fifths ▶ 분자가 2이상일 경우 분모의 서수에 s를 붙여 복수형을 만든다.   15 third → the third ▶of를 사용할 경우는 반드시 서수 앞에 the를 붙인다.

2   1 dollar → dollars ▶복수일 때 dollar에 s를 붙인다.   2 third → three ▶소수점 이하의 수는 한 자리씩 기수로 읽어 준다.   3 forty seven → four seven   4 second → half ▶1/2이라는 뜻의 half를 쓴다.   5 fortieth → forty ▶'21'부터는 일의 자리만 서수로 읽는다.   6 third → the third   7 one four → fourteen   8 eighth → eighths   9 sixteenth → sixteen   10 August 15 Thursday →

Thursday August 15 ▶요일, 월, 일, 연도 순서이다.   11 sixth → six 12 fifth → fifths ▶분자가 2이상이면 서수인 분모에 s를 붙여 복수로 만든다.   13 twelfth → twelve   14 twenty-sixth → twenty-six   15 zero → oh

실전Test   p.26~29

01 ⑤	02 ②	03 eight / eighth	04 ③
05 ②	06 twentieth → twenty	07 ①	08 ③
09 oh → zero	10 ②		

01 100이상의 숫자도 모두 서수로 만들 수 있다.
02 ①③④⑤는 서수이고 ②는 기수이다.
03 기수를 서수로 만들 때는 몇몇을 제외하고 '기수+th로 만든다.
04 four의 서수는 fourth이다.
05 학년은 순서를 나타내므로 서수를 사용한다. two → the second
06 21부터는 일의 자리만 서수로 바꿔 주면 된다.
07 소수점 이하는 한 자리씩 기수로 읽는다.
08 분자가 2이상인 경우 서수로 읽는 분모에 s를 붙여 복수로 만든다.
09 0이 맨 처음 올 때는 반드시 zero로 읽는다.
10 연도는 두 자리씩 끊어 읽는다. nineteen ninety-eight

Quiz!   p.30

1 The first   2 three   3 the fourth   4 fifty
5 the ninth   6 the second   7 fifteen

1 nineteen   2 dollars sixty-one   3 zero / four one
4 forty-seven point   5 Friday July   6 fifths

○2 비인칭주어

기초 다지기   p.34~37

① 1 What moth   2 What day   3 Do / the / time   4 date / It   5 What time   6 season / It   7 What year / It   8 How's   9 like / It   10 What is

② 1 have / It   2 month   3 date   4 weather like / It   5 day   6 time   7 time   8 weather / It   9 do / have / is it   10 season / It

③ 1 2시 3분 전   2 7시 4분   3 자정 12시   4 5시 15분   5 3시 40분   6 1시 15분 전   7 11시 25분   8 10시 15분   9 4시 30분   10 6시 7분 전

④ 1 3시 14분   2 11시 15분   3 12시 6분   4 7시 15분   5 7시 20분   6 9시 30분   7 12시 15분 전   8 7시 32분   9 11시 8분 전   10 5시 18분

꼭꼭 다지기   p.38~41

① 1 day is it   2 date is it   3 year is it   4 What's   5 the time   6 month is it   7 the weather   8 have the time ▶Do you have time? 시간 있니? Do you have the time? 몇 시니?   9 season is it   10 do you have

② 1 time is it   2 the weather   3 day is it   4 season is it   5 like   6 date is it   7 day is it   8 have time   9 the date   10 year is it

③
1 twenty five, twenty five, seven
2 twelve, ten, to   3 twelve, o'clock
4 forty, to, one
5 half, past ▶half는 after나 to와 함께 사용할 수 없다.
6 five, a quarter

④
1 three o'clock   2 oh, five, four
3 a quarter, to ▶quarter는 past, after, to와 함께 사용할 수 있다.
4 thirty-five, to, one   5 past, after
6 five, to

실력 다지기   p.42~43

① 1 weather → weather like   2 month → year   3 date → day ▶날짜를 물을 때는 date로 요일을 물을 때는 day를 사용한다.   4 the time → time ▶the 삭제 '너 시간 있니?'라고 물을 때는 time앞에 the를 쓰지 않는다.   5 This → It   6 day → season   7 That's → It's ▶명암은 비인칭주어 it으로 표현한다.   8 quarter → a quarter   9 How → What   10 like → like삭제   11 weather → weather like   12 day → date   13 How → What   14 month → season   15 the five → the fifth

② 1 Fifteen → A quarter ▶15분은 □시 □분의 순서로 나타낼 때는 fifteen을 사용하지만 past, after, to를 이용하여 □분□시로 나타낼 때는 a quarter를 사용한다.   2 time → the time   3 past → to ▶'~분 전'은 to를 이용한다.   4 to → past(after)   5 a half → half ▶a삭제 half에는 a를 붙이지 않는다.   6 That's → It's   7 after → past ▶30분을 나타낼 때 half는 after와 함께 사용하지 않는다.   8 to two a quarter → a quarter to two   9 after → to   10 to → past   11 that → it   12 it's not → I don't   13 sixteen twelve → twelve sixteen   14 quarter → a quarter   15 to → past ▶half는 past만 함께 사용할 수 있다.

실전Test   p.44~47

01 ③   02 like   03 two, past, after   04 ④
05 ④, ⑤   06 ②   07 ②   08 ⑤   09 ③
10 (A) - ⓐ, (B) - ⓑ

01 비인칭주어 It는 시간, 날씨, 날짜, 거리, 명암들을 표현할 때 사용한다.
03 □시 □분의 순서로 나타내거나 '~지난'의 의미를 갖는 past나 after로 나타낸다.

4   Grammar Joy 4

04 ㅁ시 ㅁ분 순서로 나타내거나 6시 50분은 7시 10분 전이므로 '~로 향하여'라는 의미를 지닌 to로 나타낸다.

05 15분은 ㅁ분 ㅁ시의 순서로 나타낼 때 fifteen대신에 a quarter를 사용한다.

06 ①③④⑤ 는 비인칭주어이고 ②는 지시대명사이다.

07 요일을 물을 때는 What day~?를 이용한다.

08 날짜를 물을 때는 date를 사용한다.

10 Do you have the time?은 몇 시인지를 묻는 표현이고 Do you have time?은 '너 시간 있니?'를 의미하는 표현이다.

p.48

1 What date   2 like   3 What day   4 What season
5 What year

1 thirty / half past   2 eight, past (after) eight
3 to ten   4 eight to   5 fifteen, a quarter past / a quarter after

be동사, 일반동사, 과거형의 긍정문

기초 다지기
p.53~59

①

1 am, 아프다. 현재   was, 아팠다. 과거
2 was, 였다 (이었다). 과거   is, 이다. 현재
3 worked, 일했다. 과거   works, 일한다. 현재
4 puts, 쓴다. 현재   put, 썼다. 과거
5 sent, 보냈다. 과거   sends, 보낸다. 현재

②   1 was   2 were   3 was   4 was ▶The color of the house는 3인칭 단수이므로 is의 과거 was를 쓴다.   5 were
6 were   7 were   8 was   9 were ▶Minho and Tom은 복수이므로 are의 과거 were를 쓴다.   10 were   11 was
12 was   13 were ▶The presents는 복수이므로 are의 과거 were를 쓴다.   14 was   15 were

③   1 ended   2 worked   3 lived   4 married
5 studied   6 looked   7 played   8 washed
9 enjoyed   10 pulled   11 visited   12 listened
13 liked   14 waxed   15 rained   16 worried
17 dried   18 dropped   19 smiled   20 loved
21 stopped   22 walked   23 opened   24 snowed
25 rubbed   26 prayed   27 tried   28 turned
29 carried   30 fixed

④   1 was, were   2 spoke   3 did   4 ran
5 went   6 came   7 saw   8 had   9 drank
10 made   11 began   12 said   13 swam
14 sold   15 drew   16 told   17 ate   18 found
19 gave   20 met   21 took   22 got   23 drove
24 slept   25 wrote   26 left   27 fell   28 kept
29 broke   30 sent

⑤ 1 spent 2 ran 3 felt 4 spoke 5 sat
6 had 7 lost 8 saw 9 won 10 woke
11 heard 12 was, were 13 stood 14 took
15 understood 16 made 17 did 18 swam
19 bought 20 taught 21 caught 22 wrote
23 thought 24 left 25 cut 26 fell 27 put
28 met 29 read 30 gave

⑥ 1 sent 2 drove 3 got 4 said 5 did
6 found 7 told 8 cut 9 drank 10 went
11 kept 12 lost 13 came 14 heard
15 bought 16 spent 17 sat 18 caught
19 taught 20 broke 21 slept 22 took
23 thought 24 ate 25 understood 26 fell
27 put 28 sold 29 began 30 drew

⑦ 1 am / was 2 were / are 3 wore / wears
4 wears / wore 5 read / reads 6 barked / barks
7 asks / asked

p.60~63

① 1 was ▶am, is의 과거형은 was, are의 과거형은 were이다.
2 was 3 were 4 was 5 were 6 were 7 was
8 was 9 were 10 was

② 1 walked 2 drank 3 liked 4 sat
5 heard 6 ran 7 took 8 started 9 drove
10 read

③ 1 catches / 현재 2 lost / 과거 3 stopped / 과거
4 have / 현재 5 spent / 과거 6 comes / 현재 7 gave /
과거 8 sets / 현재 9 took / 과거 10 talked / 과거

④ 1 got / 과거 2 boils / 현재 3 put / 과거 4 feels
/ 현재 5 transferred / 과거 6 says / 현재 7 fell / 과거
8 shaved / 과거 9 is / 현재 10 moves / 현재

p.64~65

① 1 were → was ▶Judy는 3인칭 단수이므로was를 쓴다.
2 draws → drew 3 falled → fell 4 was → were
5 reads → read ▶read는 현재형과 과거형이 같다. 뒤에 과거를
나타내는 부사 yesterday가 있으므로 주어인 My father가 3인칭 단수
일지라도 과거형인 read가 와야 한다. 6 was → were
7 cutted → cut ▶cut은 현재형과 과거형이 같다. 8 draws
→ drew 9 is → was 10 receive → received
11 wents → went 12 begins → began
13 speaked → spoke 14 The businessmen →
The businessman 15 do → did

② 1 dryed → dried 2 was → were 3 win →
won 4 text → texted 5 hitted → hit 6 were →
was 7 buys → bought 8 looks → looked
9 droped → dropped ▶'단모음(1모음)+단자음(1자음)' 으로 끝
나면서 뒤에 강세가 있는 경우 과거형은 마지막 자음을 한 번 더 써주고
ed를 붙인다. 10 come → came 11 women →
woman ▶was는 단수, were은 복수 뒤에 쓰는 말로, 복수형
women이 아닌 단수형woman이 와야 한다. 12 sleeps → slept
13 getted → got 14 breaked → broke 15 was
→ were

p66~69

01 ⑤ 02 ③ 03 ④ 04 ③ 05 ④ 06 ④
07 was → were 08 ④ 09 (1) watched
(2) bought (3) were 10 ⑤

03 ① sotped → stopped / ② climbbed → climbed / ③ openned →
opened / ⑤droped → dropped

04 ① carryed → carried / ② catched → caught / ④ visitted →
visited / ⑤ haved → had

05 Jane and Adam은 3인칭 복수이고, 현재를 나타내는 부사 now가
있으므로 동사는 are이 온다. The house는 3인칭 단수이고 과거를
나타내는 부사구 'last year'가 있으므로 동사는 was가 된다.

07 주어가 복수이므로 are의 과거형 were가 와야 한다.

08 현재시제의 경우 my father가 3인칭 단수이므로 put에 s가 붙지만, 과거시제의 경우 put은 현재형과 과거형의 형태가 같으므로, put이 온다.

09 주어가 1,3인칭 단수인 경우 be동사의 과거형은 was이고 주어가 복수인 경우 be동사의 과거형은 were이다. 문장의 끝의 때를 나타내는 부사와 동사의 시제를 일치시켜야 한다.

10 the day before yesterday(그저께)는 과거를 나타내는 부사구이므로 현재형 문장에는 쓸 수 없다.

p.70

1 are　2 left　3 walk　4 sold　5 puts　6 caught
7 stopped　8 was　9 began　10 gave

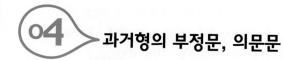

04 과거형의 부정문, 의문문

기초다지기　　　p.74~77

①

1 were, the beggars　　2 The movie, wasn't
3 Was, the mountain　　4 They, weren't
5 There, weren't　　6 Were, you
7 The comic book, wasn't
8 Were, Joe and his cousin
9 Was, the box　　　　10 This watch, wasn't

②　1 they weren't　2 it was　3 it wasn't
4 they weren't　5 she was　6 it was　7 they
weren't　8 they were　9 it wasn't　10 they were

③　1 Did, spend　2 didn't, buy　3 didn't, see
▶did, didn't 뒤에는 동사원형이 온다. some은 긍정문·권유문에, any 는 의문문·부정문에 사용된다.　4 didn't, catch　5 Did,
need　6 Did, live　7 Did, put　8 didn't, leave
9 Did, drive　10 didn't, move

④　1 didn't, do　2 Did, meet　3 Did, give
4 didn't, want　5 Did, stop　6 didn't, understand
7 Did, build　8 Did, go　9 didn't, read　10 didn't,
say

꼭꼭다지기　　　p.78~81

①

1 They, didn't, play　2 Did, she, break
3 Did, you, pick　4 His uncle, didn't, leave
5 Did, Mary, ask　6 Did, you, hear
7 He, didn't, teach
8 your daughters, didn't learn
9 Did, you, take　　10 The girl, didn't, scribble

② 1 she, did 2 he, didn't 3 they, didn't
4 it, did 5 he, did 6 she, didn't 7 we, did
8 it, didn't 9 I, didn't 10 I, did

③

1 are / 현재. Are, your parents, they, are
2 was / 과거. Was, the woman, she, wasn't
3 is / 현재. My tooth, isn't
4 were / 과거. Were, your cousins, they, were
5 were / 과거. The boys, weren't
6 is / 현재. Is, James, he, is
7 were / 과거. Were, there, there, weren't
8 was / 과거. The man, wasn't
9 was / 과거. It, wasn't
10 are / 현재. Are, they, they, aren't

④

1 lost / 과거. Did, you, lose, I, didn't
2 introduced / 과거. I, didn't, introduce
3 costs / 현재. Does, the cap cost, it, does
4 wants / 현재. Does, the man, want, he, doesn't
5 saw / 과거. The visitors, didn't, see
6 had / 과거. Jane, didn't, have
7 took / 과거. Did, he, take, he, did
8 felt / 과거. Did, you, feel, I, did
9 change / 현재. Leaves, don't, change,
10 sat / 과거. Did, he, sit, he, didn't

p.82~83

① 1 was → were 2 works → work 3 were → was 4 putted → put ▶put의 과거는 put이다. 5 found → find 6 had not → didn't have 7 reads → read ▶문장 끝에 과거를 나타내는 부사 last, yesterday, ago등이 오면 동사의 시제를 과거로 나타내야 한다. 8 visits → visit 9 lost not → didn't lose 10 don't → didn't 11 Does → did 12 are → were 13 lived → live 14 was → were 15 selled → sold ▶sell의 과거는 sold이다.

② 1 lie → lay 2 sended → sent ▶send의 과거는 sent이다. 3 does not → didn't 4 make → made 5 Did → Was 6 cuts → cut ▶cut의 과거는 cut이다. 7 spent → spend ▶앞에 did가 나왔으므로 뒤에는 동사원형이 와야 한다. 8 rubs → rub 9 doesn't → didn't 10 got → get 11 had not → didn't have 12 did → was 13 sleeped → slept ▶sleep의 과거는 slept이다. 14 are → were 15 hits → hit ▶hit의 과거는 hit이다.

실전Test

p.84~87

01 ③ 02 ④ 03 ③ 04 ③, ⑤ 05 ⑤
06 They were not(weren't) happy then. 07 My brother did not (didn't) break the window.
08 ③ 09 made → make 10 ⑤

01 일반동사 과거의 부정문에는 didn't를 써야 한다.

02 주어진 문장들은 어제의 일과이므로 현재형 take로 표현할 수 없다. take의 과거형인 took를 사용해야 한다.

04 과거 시제로 물으면 과거 시제로 대답하며 he는 3인칭 단수이므로 is의 과거 was를 사용한다.

05 did, didn't 뒤에는 동사원형이 온다.

06 be동사의 과거형 문장의 부정문은 be동사 뒤에 not만 붙이면 된다.

07 주어+didn't+동사원형

08 Did로 물었으므로 Yes, I did또는 No, I didn't로 대답한다.

09 Did뒤에는 동사원형이 온다.

10 시제가 과거일 때 did 또는 didn't 뒤에는 동사원형이 온다.

Quiz!

p88

1 Was the soldier, he was.
2 She didn't want
3 Did he hear, he didn't
4 Did Susan open, she did.
5 Mr. Kim and Mrs. Kim didn't sell
6 We weren't
7 Did your sister memorize, she did.

8 The girl didn't understand

9 This dog didn't swim

10 Did Inho listen, he didn't.

Review Test 1
p.90~P97

Unit 1

01

1 three **2** seventh **3** fourth **4** one **5** fifth
6 six **7** second

02

1 nineteen eighty-eight

2 August twenty

3 zero one oh-three one oh nine

4 twenty-five point seven four

5 twelve dollars sixty eight cents

6 two thirds

7 Sunday June twenty-fifth

03

1 fifteen **2** the second **3** one **4** the fifth
5 eleven **6** four **7** the third

04

1 one two **2** twenty-four(fourth) **3** twenty,
fifteen **4** fifths **5** thousand fifteen **6** zero, oh,
seven, oh **7** July, eighteen seventeen

Unit 2

01

1 How **2** time **3** day **4** date **5** time
6 the time **7** What **8** time

02

1 2시 50분 **2** 9시 7분 **3** 7시 6분 전 **4** 3시 15분 전 **5** 10시 30분

03

1 What time **2** What day **3** What date, What,
date **4** What, How **5** do, have

04

1 9, 20, eight, forty, twenty, nine

2 12, 10, eleven, fifty, ten, twelve

3 nine, fifteen, a quarter, nine

4 two, thirty, half, two

5 midnight

Unit 3

01

1 was **2** was **3** were **4** are **5** was **6** is
7 was

02

1 cleaned **2** studies **3** visited **4** is swimming
5 played

03

1 was, 과거 **2** was, 과거 **3** am, 현재 **4** were, 과거
5 is, 현재

04

1 came, 과거 **2** took, 과거 **3** is snowing, 현재진행
4 bought, 과거 **5** has, 현재

Unit 4

01

1 He, wasn't **2** Was, she **3** They, weren't
4 Was, the game **5** There, wasn't

02

1 They, didn't, like **2** Did, Tom, go **3** I, didn't,
have **4** Did, she, sell **5** Her family, didn't, live

03

1 he, was **2** she, did **3** they, didn't **4** they,
weren't **5** it, was **6** she, didn't **7** he, was
8 he, didn't **9** they, were **10** I/We, didn't

내/신/대/비
p.98~102

01 ④ ▶①②③⑤는 서수, ④는 기수 **02** four, fourth
03 ② ▶소수점 이하는 하나씩 기수로 읽는다. **04** ③ ▶분자가 2
이상일 경우 분모의 서수에 s를 붙여 복수형을 만든다. **05** ①
06 five and two ninths **07** ③ ▶①②④⑤는 비인칭주어,
③는 지시대명사 **08** What **09** ④ ▶Do you have tine?은 '시
간이 있니?'라는 표현이다. **10** season **11** ③ **12** fifteen,

a quarter, a quarter **13** ④ **14** ⑤ ▶동사의 시제가 과거를 나타내므로 과거를 나타내는 부사(구)를 써야한다. **15** ③ **16** ③ ▶동사의 시제는 현재인데 부사구는 과거를 나타낸다. **17 was, lost 18** ② **19** ⑤ ▶과거를 나타내는 단수 be동사가 와야 한다. **20 Do, Was 21** ⑤ **22 didn't do 23** ③ ▶① ②④⑤는 Did, ③는 Was를 써야 한다. **24** ④ **25 Does Tom have**

05 과거진행형

p.106~107

1 was learning, 과거진행형, 배우고 있는 중이었다,
am learning, 현재진행형, 배우고 있는 중이다
2 are walking, 현재진행형, 산책 시키고 있는 중이다,
were walking, 과거진행형, 산책시키고 있는 중이었다.
3 is having, 현재진행형, 먹고 있는 중이다,
was having, 과거진행형, 먹고 있는 중이었다.
4 were working, 과거진행형, 일하고 있는 중이었다,
are working, 현재진행형, 일하고 있는 중이다.
5 is snowing, 현재진행형, 오고 있는 중이다,
was snowing, 과거진행형, 오고 있는 중이었다.

②

1 was fixing **2** were skating **3** were planting
4 was baking **5** was standing **6** was eating
7 were watching **8** was laughing
9 was holding **10** were exercising

p.108~111

1 현재진행, is snoring **2** 과거진행, were making
3 현재진행, are looking **4** 현재진행, am playing
5 과거진행, was coughing **6** 현재진행, are spending
7 현재진행, is surfing **8** 과거진행, were giving
9 과거진행, was dying **10** 과거진행, were making

②

1 과거진행, was watching **2** 과거진행, was typing
3 과거진행, was drinking **4** 현재진행, are jogging
5 현재진행, are chatting **6** 과거진행, were writing
7 현재진행, is using **8** 현재진행, are sleeping
9 현재진행, am setting **10** 현재진행, is chasing

③

1 He wasn't playing
2 Was your daughter washing
3 I wasn't doing
4 Was your aunt peeling
5 They weren't taking
6 Were many people running
7 Were two taxis coming
8 Maria wasn't making
9 Was John pouring
10 Bill and his friend weren't playing

④ 1 she wasn't 2 they weren't 3 they were
4 she was 5 I wasn't 6 he was 7 they weren't
8 he(she) wasn't 9 she was 10 they were

실력 다지기 p.112~113

① 1 am → was 2 were → is 3 buy → buying
4 Does → Was 5 were → is 6 cut → cutting
7 did → were 8 were → are 9 was → is
10 checking → was checking

② 1 take → taking 2 did → was 3 Were →
Are 4 using → was using 5 was → is 6 were →
were 삭제 7 Did → Were 8 didn't → weren't
9 are → were 10 weren't → wasn't

실전Test p.114~117

01 ③ 02 ② 03 ⑤ 04 ③ 05 We weren't
making a snowman. 06 ③ 07 ① 08 I was
doing yoga in my room. 09 He and she were
washing their hands. 10 ④

02 ① were → was ③ were → was ④ was → were ⑤ was → were

03 과거진행형이다.

04 Was로 물으면 was로 대답한다.

05 과거진행형의 부정문은 wasn't나 weren't를 사용한다.

06 ①was → were ② didn't → wasn't ④ study → studying ⑤ was
→ were

07 동사의 시제가 과거진행형이므로 과거를 나타내는 부사(구)가 와야
한다.

08 I는 단수이므로 'was+~ing'를 써야 한다.

09 He and she는 복수이므로 'were+~ing'를 써야 한다.

10 '팔고 있다'는 현재진행형이므로 '팔고 있었다'로 옮겨야 한다.

 p.118

1 was waxing 2 are speaking 3 are traveling
4 was playing 5 were crossing 6 were fighting
7 was flying 8 am calling 9 was drawing
10 is shaving

 **미래형**

기초다지기 p.123-125

①

1 will do, 미래. 할 것이다.

did, 과거. 했다

is going to do, 미래. 할 예정이다.

does, 현재. 한다

2 reads, 현재. 읽는다

is going to read, 미래. 읽을 예정이다.

read, 과거. 읽었다.

will read, 미래. 읽을 것이다.

3 looked after, 과거. 돌보았다

looks after, 현재. 돌본다

is going to look after, 미래. 돌볼 예정이다

will look after, 미래. 돌볼 것이다.

② **1** sing **2** be ▶will+동사원형 / am, are, is의 동사원형은 be이다. **3** study **4** dig **5** take **6** take
7 hunt **8** make **9** rides **10** be **11** buy
12 be **13** take **14** fly **15** capture

③ **1** will, play **2** will, call **3** will, be ▶will+동사원형 / is의 동사원형은 be이다. **4** will, be **5** will, be

1 is, going, to, snow **2** is, going, to, take
3 is, going, to, move **4** is, going, to, see
5 is, going, to, pay

꼭꼭다지기 p.126~131

①

1 are, going, to, take **2** will, wear
3 is, going, to, sell **4** are, going, to, have
5 will, talk **6** will, get
7 is, going, to, invite **8** are, going, to, follow
9 will, see **10** is, going, to, exercise

②

1 will play, played, is going to play, plays
2 takes, will take, is going to take, took
3 are going to paint, painted, paint, will paint
4 will travel, are going to travel, traveled, travel

③

1 will paint/am going to paint, 미래
2 will call/is going to call, 미래
3 read, 과거 **4** will be, 미래
5 use, 현재 **6** was, 과거
7 will quit /is going to quit, 미래
8 composed, 과거
9 will ski/are going to ski, 미래
10 waits, 현재

④

1 bought, 과거
2 will carry/am going to carry. 미래
3 will plant/am going to plant, 미래
4 will travel/is going to travel, 미래
5 made, 과거
6 will be/is going to be, 미래
7 opened, 과거
8 will clean/are going to clean, 미래
9 uses, 현재
10 don't remember, 현재

⑤

1 Tomorrow won't be **2** Will she skip
3 Jane won't wear **4** I won't eat
5 Will they sit

1 I am not going to see
2 He is not going to sweep
3 Are they going to eat
4 The cell phone is not going to disappear
5 Are you going to take

6 1 he will 2 they will 3 she won't
4 I won't 5 we will

1 I am 2 she is 3 he isn't 4 he isn't
5 they aren't

실력다지기
p.132~133

1 1 makes → make 2 went → will go 3 are
→ be ▶will+동사원형 / am, are, is의 동사원형은 be이다.
4 keeps → keep 5 going → am going 6 willn't
→ won't 7 go → going 8 buys → buy 9 is
going to → will 10 leave → leaving 11 turn →
to turn 12 is → be 13 wins → win 14 have → to
have 15 am → will be

2 1 be → will be 2 go → going 3 tells → tell
4 Is → Are 5 going → going to 6 pays → pay
7 going → am going 8 ends → end 9 arrive →
arriving 10 speaks → speak 11 is → are 12 is
going to → will 13 go → going 14 Did → Will
15 go → going

실전Test
p.134~137

01 ② 02 ② 03 ⑤ 04 ④ 05 ④ 06 is
going to 07 ③ 08 ② 09 missed 10 ①

01 be going to의 부정문은 be동사 바로 뒤에 not을 붙이면 된다.

02 be going to로 물으면 be going to로 대답한다.

03 미래형 문장에는 과거를 나타내는 부사(last Saturday)는 사용할 수 없다.

04 will 다음엔 동사원형이 온다.

05 be going to 뒤에는 동사 원형이 온다.

06 will과 be going to는 미래를 나타낸다는 점에서 같다.

07 Is she~?로 질문하면 Yes, she is. 또는 No, she isn't. 로 대답한다.

08 Will you~?로 질문하면 Yes, I will. 또는 No, I will not.으로 대답해야 한다.

09 과거시제(yesterday)를 나타내므로 missed를 사용한다.

10 be going to 다음에 동사원형이 와야 한다.

Quiz
p.138

1 You will be ten years old, Will you be ten years old?
2 I will help you, I won't help you.
3 He is going to play Taekwondo, He isn't going to play Taekwondo.
4 She is going to see a doctor, Is she going to see a doctor?

1 They are going to bring some books.
2 Susan will meet him tonight.
3 He will take a bus.
4 I am going to wash the dishes.
5 She will buy a computer.

 **감탄문**

p.142~145

①

1 this is, What, farm　**2** it is, What, fox
3 the movie is, How　**4** she, has, What, flowers
▶a가 없어도 pretty뒤에 복수형 명사인 flowers가 있으므로 what을 이용한 감탄문을 만들어야 한다.　**5** she runs, How　**6** they are, What, clocks　**7** he is, How　**8** they are, What, melons ▶melons가 복수이기 때문에 a가 없어도 sweet뒤에 명사가 있으므로 what을 이용한 감탄문을 만들어야 한다.　**9** his father is, What, man　**10** those are, What, problems
11 Picasso is, How　**12** these are, What, games
13 the pot is, How　**14** the restaurants are, How
▶nice뒤에 수식받는 명사가 없으므로 how를 이용한 의문문을 만들어야 한다. the restaurants는 주어에 해당한다.　**15** this is, What, room

②

1 How / cute / this doggy / is!
2 How / beautiful / the girl / is!
3 How / easily / he / can swim!
4 How / fun / this cartoon book / is!
5 How / expensive / this / is!
6 How / happy / you / look!

③

1 orange, What / a / sweet / orange / this / is!
2 oranges, What / sweet / oranges / these / are!
3 country, What / a / big / country / Russia / is!
4 buildings, What / tall / buildings / those / are!
5 clock, What / an / old / clock / you / have! ▶very가 what으로 바뀌어가면서 old앞에 부정관사가 오게 되므로 an을 붙여 준다.
6 clerk, What / a / kind / clerk / he / is!

④

1 game, What / an / exciting / game / that / is! ▶
very가 what으로 바뀌면서 exciting 앞에 부정관사가 오게 되므로 an을 붙여 준다.
2 cake, What / a / delicious / cake / he / made!
3 dolphins, What / smart / dolphins / those / are!
4 How / well / Judy / played / the cello!
5 How / nicely / they / performed!
6 How / wild / tigers / are!

p.146~149

①

1 What a clever boy, you are!
2 How long, her hair was!
3 How big, his feet are!
4 What a strong man, Samson was!
5 How tall, those sunflowers are!
6 What lovely dresses, these are!
7 How poor, the kitten is!
8 How slow, it goes!
9 What an excellent teacher, she was!
10 What a cheap vase, it is!

②

1 How big, this tower was!
2 How dangerous, the oven is!
3 What a great artist, Picasso is!
4 What a fine day, it was!
5 How rich, Bill Gates is!
6 What foolish animals, bears are!
7 What an ugly doll, that is!
8 How well, she can speak Japanese!
9 What a dirty shoes, these are!
10 How slow, he is walking!

3

1 What an important thing, it is! ▶very가 what으로 바뀌면서 부정관사가 important 앞으로 오게 되므로 an을 사용한다.

2 What important things, those are!

3 How fast, she cooks curry and rice!

4 How intelligent, they are!

5 What a small face, Jane has!

6 What a diligent woman, his mother is!

7 What a deep lake, this is!

8 How clean, this lake is!

9 How slow, turtles are!

10 What heavy boxes, those are! ▶부정관사 a가 없어도 boxes라는 복수명사가 있기 때문에 what을 이용한 감탄문을 만들어야 한다.

4

1 What a sweet pumpkin that is!

2 How sad Mary looks!

3 What a light jumper this is!

4 What wonderful boats these are!

5 How hot this coffee is!

6 What a fashionable shirt I bought!

7 What a sharp knife this is!

8 How cold this room is!

9 What an interesting story it is! ▶very가 what으로 바뀌면서 부정관사가 interesting앞으로 오게 되므로 an을 써야 한다.

10 How full she is!

p.150~151

1　1 How → What ▶감탄하는 부분이 명사(chocolate)를 포함하는 경우, what을 사용한다. 셀 수 없는 명사 / 복수형 명사 앞에는 부정관사(a/an)를 사용할 수 없다. **2** What → How **3** a → an **4** a → a 삭제 **5** a → a 삭제 **6** How → What **7** jumped she → she jumped **8** a → a 삭제 ▶stew는 셀 수 없는 명사이므로 a나 an을 사용할 수 없다. **9** good → well **10** a → a 삭제 **11** handsome boy → a handsome boy **12** What → How **13** What → How **14** children → child **15** How → What

2　**1** How → What **2** a → an **3** is the musician → the musician is ▶'How+형용사+동사+주어'는 의문문으로 '!'가 오기 위해선 'How+형용사+주어+동사!'의 순서가 되어야 한다.

4 woman → women **5** What → How **6** an unkind → unkind **7** What famous man → What a famous man **8** What → How **9** is this → this is **10** a → a 삭제 **11** What → How **12** very → very 삭제 ▶very가 what으로 바뀐 것이므로 very는 없애야 한다. **13** What → How **14** How → What **15** an → a

실전Test
p.152~155

01 ③　02 ⑤　03 How well Mary swims
04 ②　05 How → What　06 ②　07 ④
08 (A) ⓑ, (B) ⓐ　09 ④　10 How sick my mother is!

01 What+a(an)+형+명+주+동!, How+형+주+동!

02 happily는 happy의 부사형이므로 뒤에 나오는 명사 girl을 꾸며 줄 수 없다.

03 How+부사+주어+동사!

04 What으로 시작하는 감탄문은 'What+a(n)+형용사+명사+주어+동사'의 어순이다.

05 형용사 old뒤에 paintings라는 명사가 있으므로 What으로 시작하는 감탄문을 만들어야 한다.

06 How big this pizza is!

07 they are가 복수를 나타내므로 painter는 복수형인 painters가 되어야 한다.

08 'How+형+주+동!'은 감탄문이고, 'How+형+동+주?'는 의문문이다.

09 expensive가 모음 e의 소리로 시작하므로 관사 an이 와야 한다.

10 How+형+주+동!

1 What a big elephant it is!
2 How short she is!
3 What an exciting game that is!
4 What a comfortable sofa he has!
5 What wonderful pictures they are!
6 How young my father looks!
7 How well Jim can play the cello!
8 How long the train is!
9 What a cute girl my sister is!
10 How busy they are!

부정의문문, 부가의문문

기초다지기

p.160~163

1

1 현재, be동사. Isn't
2 과거, 일반동사. Didn't ▶bought는 buy의 과거이므로 Didn't가 맨 앞에 오고 뒤에 buy가 와야 한다.
3 현재, 일반동사. Doesn't   4 현재, 일반동사. Doesn't
5 미래, 일반동사. Won't   6 현재, 일반동사. Doesn't
7 과거, 일반동사. Didn't   8 현재, be동사. Aren't
9 과거, be동사. Wasn't   10 미래, 일반동사. Won't

2   1 Yes, it, does   2 No, he, wasn't
3 Yes, she, did   4 No, I, don't   5 Yes, they, can
6 Yes, there, are   7 No, I, wasn't   8 No, it, didn't
9 Yes, he, will   10 No, it, isn't

3

1 현재, aren't, 미래, won't, 현재, are, 과거, were
2 현재, doesn't, 과거, didn't, 현재, does, 과거, did
3 명령문, will you ▶명령문의 부가의문문에는 will you?가 온다.
   현재, does, 과거, did, 현재, doesn't
4 현재, does, 과거, didn't, 과거, did, 권유문, shall we ▶권유문의 부가의문문에는 shall we?가 온다.

4

1 doesn't he, do they, didn't they, did they
2 isn't she, is she, wasn't she, was she
3 won't you, will you, shall we, will you
4 weren't they, are they, aren't they, were they

① 1 Isn't 2 No, she can't 3 Won't ▶will not의 축약형은 won't 4 Yes, they are 5 Wasn't 6 Can't 7 No, he doesn't 8 Don't 9 Yes, she will 10 Aren't

② 1 doesn't, she 2 is, it 3 shall, we ▶권유문의 부가의문문에는 shall we?가 온다. 4 wasn't, he 5 does, he 6 were, you 7 won't, she 8 did, they 9 didn't, he ▶주어 Her brother가 3인칭 단수인데 put에 s가 붙지 않았으므로 과거를 나타낸다. 10 does, she 11 do, they 12 will, you ▶명령문의 부가의문문에는 will you?가 온다. 13 does, she 14 can't, he 15 are, you

③ 1 doesn't, she 2 shall, we 3 will, you 4 were, they 5 aren't, we 6 do, you 7 won't, she ▶Amy는 she로 받는다. 8 didn't, they ▶The policemen은 복수이므로 they로 받는다. 9 will, you 10 don't, you 11 is, he 12 does, she 13 wasn't, she 14 weren't, you 15 can't, he

④ 1 do, you, No, I don't 2 will, you 3 won't, you, No, I won't ▶will not의 축약형은 won't이다. 4 isn't, she, Yes, she, is 5 didn't, he, Yes, he, did 6 shall, we 7 are, they, Yes, they, are 8 can't, he, Yes, he, can ▶Mr. Bush는 he로 받는다. 9 did, he, No, he, didn't ▶Tommy는 he로 받는다. 10 doesn't, she, Yes, she, does

① 1 aren't they → don't they ▶cross가 일반동사이므로 don't가 와야 한다. 2 will you → shall we 3 didn't she → did she 4 don't they → weren't they 5 does he → did he ▶부가의문문에서는 앞 뒤의 시제를 일치시켜야 한다. 6 shall we → will you 7 does she → doesn't she 8 didn't Judy → didn't she ▶Judy는 she로 받는다. 9 are there → aren't there ▶앞이 긍정이면 뒤

는 부정이 되어야 한다. 10 shall we → will you 11 weren't they → aren't they 12 hadn't she → didn't she 13 was he → is he 14 don't you → aren't you 15 aren't Tom and Judy → aren't they ▶Tom and Judy는 they로 받는다.

② 1 do they → don't they ▶babies는 they로 받는다. 2 wasn't he → won't he 3 won't you → will you 4 do they → didn't they 5 will we → shall we 6 didn't you → did you 7 was she → didn't she 8 did she → doesn't she 9 weren't there → aren't there 10 did he → didn't he 11 aren't my students → aren't they ▶my students는 they로 받는다. 12 do you → will you 13 didn't you → don't you 14 weren't you → didn't they ▶came이 일반동사의 과거형이므로 be동사의 과거형이 아니라 didn't를 써야 한다. 15 don't we → shall we

실전Test

01 ② 02 ④ 03 did → do 04 ④ 05 ③ 06 ⑤ 07 ③ 08 ⑤ 09 (A) ⓒ (B) ⓐ 10 doesn't Bill → doesn't he

01 A의 물음이 긍정으로 묻는 의문문이 될 수도 있으나 B의 대답을 만족시키기 위해서는 don't 가 되어야 한다.

02 B가 당시 A의 전화 번호를 몰랐으므로 부정의 대답이 와야 한다. 그리고 시제가 과거이므로 과거로 대답해야 한다.

03 현재로 묻는 부정의문문이므로 현재형 do로 대답해야 한다.

04 draw가 일반동사이고 주어가 3인칭 단수이므로 Doesn't를 써야 한다.

05 my father는 3인칭 단수이고 뒤에는 angry가 오므로 Isn't를 써야 한다.

07 went가 일반동사의 과거형이며 긍정문이므로 뒤에 didn't가 오고, my uncle은 대명사 he로 받아 준다.

08 부가의문문의 앞 부분이 be동사의 부정문이므로 (is not), 뒤에는 be동사의 긍정으로 의문문을 붙여야 한다.

09 Let's 로 시작하는 권유문의 부가의문문에는 shall we?를, 명령문으로 시작하는 부가의문문에는 will you?를 덧붙여 만든다.

10 부가의문문에서는 주어 (Bill)를 대명사(he)로 받아 준다.

p.174

1 doesn't he   **2** weren't you   **3** can't they
4 does she   **5** will you   **6** isn't she   **7** didn't he
8 will he   **9** can they   **10** didn't he   **11** shall we
12 wasn't she   **13** is he   **14** won't he   **15** did I

Review Test 2

p.176~183

Unit 5

01
1 was, reading   **2** was, sleeping   **3** were, playing
4 was, studying   **5** were, swimming

02
1 He, was, doing   **2** Mom, was, shopping
3 We, were, going   **4** My uncle, was, washing
5 They, were, cleaning

03
1 He, wasn't, doing
2 Was, she, brushing, she was
3 We, weren't, watching
4 Were, they, taking, they were
5 I, wasn't, going
6 Was, dad, reading, he, wasn't
7 It, wasn't, snowing
8 Was, the dog, eating, it, wasn't
9 We, weren't, working
10 Was, Sumi, writing, she, was

Unit 6

01
1 will, buy   **2** is, visit   **3** are, build   **4** will, make
5 will, be

02
1 are going to have   **2** am gong to take
3 will watch   **4** is going to ride   **5** will learn

03
1 He, won't, come
2 Will, she, make, she, will
3 He, isn't, going, to, walk
4 Are, they, going, to, swim, they, are
5 I, won't, be
6 Is, Jane, going, to, clean, she, isn't
7 It, won't, rain
8 Will, Tom, play, he, won't
9 We, aren't, going, to, sing
10 Are, you, going, to, be, I, am

Unit 7

01
1 How   **2** What   **3** How   **4** What   **5** What
6 How   **7** What

02
1 How pretty the baby is
2 What a wise king he is
3 How long the tunnel is
4 What an interesting story it is
5 What tall trees these are

03
1 How fast   **2** What a thick book
3 How great   **4** What an exciting game
5 What difficult problems

04
1 How boring the movie is
2 What a deep lake this is
3 What brave fire-fighters they are
4 How small the puppies are
5 What an important person she is

Unit 8

01
1 Don't / Yes   **2** Wasn't / No   **3** Isn't / No
4 Didn't / Yes   **5** Isn't / Yes   **6** Don't / Yes
7 Wasn't / No

02
1 isn't 2 are 3 wasn't 4 didn't 5 did
6 will, you 7 shall, we

03
1 Isn't, she, she is 2 Don't, you, know, I, don't
3 Wasn't, it, it, was 4 Weren't they, they, weren't
5 Didn't, Tom, hear, he did

04
1 isn't, he, he, is 2 doesn't, she, she, doesn't
3 won't, he, he, will 4 was, she, she, was
5 did, you, I, didn't 6 isn't, there, there, is
7 does, it, it, doesn't

내/신/대/비 2 p.184~188

01 ② **02** ③ ▶I의 be동사 과거는 was이다. **03** ⑤ **04** ①
05 Mom wasn't driving a car. **06** were studying in the library **07** ④ ▶조동사 will뒤에는 동사원형이 와야 한다.
08 ⑤ ▶will not의 축약형은 won't이다. **09** ④ ▶미래를 나타내는 동사이므로 미래를 나타내는 부사(구)가 와야 한다. **10** ①
11 ④ ▶① is going to not → is not going to ② Does he going to → Is he going to ③ keeps → keep ⑤ will삭제 **12** ③ ▶will로 물었으므로 will not(won't)로 대답한다. **13** isn't going to play ▶will = be going to **14** ②⑤ **15** ① **16** ① ▶a가 있으므로 뒤의 명사는 단수가 와야 한다. **17** How thick this book is! **18** ④ ▶they are → it is **19** (A) is the boy (B) the boy is ▶'의문사+형용사+주어+동사'는 감탄문, '의문사+형용사+동사+주어'는 의문문이다. **20** What an exciting game it is!
21 ④ **22** ④ **23** ④ **24** Doesn't → Don't **25** she did

종합문제 1회 p.190~193

종합문제 1회 p.190~193

01 ② **02** ③ **03** ④ **04** ⑤ **05** four oh one - two three two five **06** ③ **07** ②, ④ **08** to
09 ③ **10** ③ **11** ⑤ **12** ① **13** They weren't having fun. **14** ⑤ **15** ④ **16** ④ **17** ③
18 ② **19** ① **20** ①

01 5th : fifth
02 서수는 순서를 나타낸다. first는 '우선'이라는 뜻의 부사로도 쓰인다.
03 월, 일, 연도 순으로 나타낸다.
04 ①, ② 분자는 기수로, 분모는 서수로 읽는다. ③, ④분자가 2이상이면 분모(서수)를 복수형으로 나타낸다.
05 전화 번호는 한 자리씩 기수로 읽는다.
06 날씨는 비인칭 주어 it으로 나타낸다.
07 ①, ⑤ half는 after나 to와 함께 사용하지 않는다. ③ half앞에는 a를 붙이지 않는다.
09 (A) Do you have time?은 '시간 있니?'라는 표현이고, (B)는 Do you have the time?은 '몇 시니?'라는 표현이다.
10 ① 3시 5분전-It's five to three. ② 4시 14분-It's fourteen past(after) four. ④ 10시 20분-It's twenty past(after)ten. ⑤ 9시 15분-It's nine fifteen.
19 I의 be동사 과거형은 was이다.
20 cut은 현재형과 과거형이 같다.

종합문제 2회 p.194~197

01 ② **02** ④ **03** ①④ **04** ① **05** Were → Was **06** are going to **07** I won't carry the luggage. **08** ⑤ **09** ④⑤ **10** ④ **11** ⑤
12 ③ **13** ④ **14** What an old watch this is!
15 ③ **16** How beautiful my wife is! **17** ⑤
18 ④ **19** Yes, I am **20** ②

01 be동사(과거형)의 부정문은 be동사 뒤에 not만 붙이면 된다.
02 일반동사 과거형의 의문문은 do나 does 대신 과거형인 did를 사용하여 만들고 뒤에 오는 일반동사는 원형이 와야 한다.

03 be동사(과거)로 질문하면 be동사(과거)로 대답하고, 일반동사(과거)로 질문하면 일반동사(과거)로 대답한다.

04 didn't 다음에는 동사원형이 온다.

05 the doctor는 3인칭 단수이므로 Was를 써야 한다.

06 will = be going to

07 will 이 들어간 문장의 부정문은 will 뒤에 not만 붙이면 된다.

08 be going to 뒤에는 동사원형이 온다.

09 Will~?에 대한 대답은 Yes,~will. 또는 No,~will not.으로 대답한다.

10 주어의 의지와는 상관 없이 이루어지는 객관적 사실의 미래형을 나타낼 때 will을 쓴다.

11 Tom을 he로 받아 주어야 한다.

12 ①②④⑤는 What을, ③은 How를 써야 한다.

14 What으로 시작하는 감탄문은 'What+a(n)+형+명+주+동!'순이다.

15 주어(these)가 복수이므로, candy는 복수형인 candies가 되어야 한다.

18 run이 일반동사이므로 doesn't가 문장 앞에 오며, 뒤에 오는 일반동사는 원형이 와야 한다.

Quizbook

Grammar joy 4

이종저

POLY BOOKS

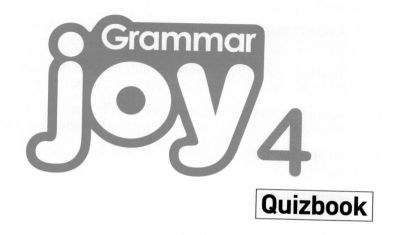

Quizbook

POLY BOOKS

01	**visa** 명 비자	she got her fourth visa. 그녀는 네 번째 비자를 얻었다.
02	**book report** 명 독후감	Tommy writes a book report for homework. Tommy는 숙제로 독후감을 쓴다.
03	**mall** 명 쇼핑센터	They are shopping at the mall. 그들은 쇼핑센터에서 쇼핑을 하고 있다.
04	**wedding day** 명 결혼기념일	James will buy flowers for his wedding day. James는 결혼기념일을 위해 꽃다발을 살 것이다.
05	**grade** 명 학년	Peter is in the third grade. Peter는 3학년이다.
06	**middle school** 명 중학교	She and I went to the same middle school. 그녀와 나는 같은 중학교를 다녔다.
07	**direction** 명 방향, 지시	Remember the direction. 지시를 기억해라.
08	**at the age of** ~의 나이에	He became a president at the age of 50. 그는 50의 나이에 대통령이 되었다.
09	**floor** 명 (건물의) 층, 바닥	The office is on the fifth floor. 사무실은 5층에 있다.
10	**surround** 동 둘러싸다	They surrounded her to give her a make up. 그들은 그녀에게 화장을 해주기 위해 둘러쌌다.
11	**be over** 끝나다	The game is over now. 그 게임은 방금 끝났다.
12	**finger** 명 손가락	We have 10 fingers. 우리는 손가락이 10개이다.
13	**dollar** 명 (화폐 단위) 달러	They spend 6 dollars. 그들은 6달러를 쓴다.
14	**soft drink** 명 탄산음료	John drinks soft drink when he eats hamburg John은 햄버거를 먹을 때 탄산음료를 마신다.
15	**member** 명 구성원	She is a member of the club. 그녀는 그 클럽의 구성원이다.

01	**sand castle** 명 모래성	Nancy and I are making a sand castle. Nancy와 나는 모래성을 만들고 있다.
02	**write in answer** 답장하다	Ailey writes in answer to a letter. Ailey는 편지에 답장을 한다.
03	**E.T** 명 외계인	They are making a movie about E.T. 그들은 외계인에 대한 영화를 만들고 있다.
04	**point** 명 점, (뾰족한) 끝	It is 2 point 5 centimeters. 2.5 센티미터이다.
05	**run after** 뒤쫓다	He runs after me. 그가 나를 뒤쫓는다.
06	**pine tree** 명 소나무	We like the pine tree. 우리는 그 소나무를 좋아한다.
07	**alarm clock** 명 자명종	The alarm clock wakes me up. 그 자명종은 나를 깨운다.
08	**robber** 명 강도	Did he meet a robber on the way home? 그는 집에 가는 길에 강도를 만났니?
09	**make ramen** 라면을 끓이다	My brother will make ramen at 11 pm. 나의 남동생은 밤 11시에 라면을 끓일 것이다.
10	**see a doctor** 진찰을 받다	Blair sees a doctor because he is sick. Blair는 아프기 때문에 진찰을 받는다.
11	**monthly rent** 명 월세	Ms. Jefferson pays monthly rent at the end of the month. Ms. Jefferson은 매달의 마지막 날에 월세를 낸다.
12	**crosswalk** 명 횡단보도	Is he walking on the crosswalk? 그는 횡단보도 위에서 걷고 있니?
13	**still object** 명 정물	Nancy draws still objects. Nancy는 정물을 그린다.
14	**spell** 동 철자를 말하다	He can spell every word on the textbook. 그는 그 교과서에 있는 모든 단어의 철자를 말할 수 있다.
15	**City Hall** 명 시청	The woman goes to the City Hall. 그 여자는 시청에 간다.

3

01	**hundred** 명 백	There are hundreds of people at the plaza. 그 광장에는 수 백 명의 사람들이 있다.
02	**thousand** 명 천	Jimmy doesn't have one thousand dollars. Jimmy는 천 달러를 가지고 있지 않다.
03	**quarter** 명 4분의 1, 15분, 25센트	It's a quarter to ten. 10시 15분 전이다.
04	**half** 명 2분의 1, 절반, 30분	I divided the pie in half. 나는 그 파이를 절반으로 나눴다.
05	**past** 형 지나간	It's half past two. 2시 30분이다.
06	**month** 명 (한) 달	What month does your teacher leave? 너의 선생님은 몇월에 떠나시니?
07	**January** 명 1월	My store opens in January. 나의 가게는 1월에 오픈한다.
08	**February** 명 2월	The next month is February. 다음 달은 2월이다.
09	**March** 명 3월	Her birthday is in March. 그녀의 생일은 3월이다.
10	**April** 명 4월	Nancy and I will leave here before April. Nancy와 나는 4월전에 여기를 떠날 것이다.
11	**May** 명 5월	Mr. Lee plans to buy a car in May. Mr. Lee는 5월에 차를 사려고 계획한다.
12	**June** 명 6월	The sky gets dark slowly in June. 6월에는 하늘이 천천히 어두워진다.
13	**July** 명 7월	Today's date is July 2nd. 오늘의 날짜는 7월 2일이다.
14	**August** 명 8월	Blair went to Seoul in August. Blair는 8월에 서울에 갔었다.
15	**September** 명 9월	Tomorrow is the last day of September. 내일은 9월의 마지막 날이다.

01	**October** 명 10월	Leaves fall in October. 10월에 낙엽이 떨어진다.
02	**November** 명 11월	The cold wind starts to blow in November. 11월에는 찬바람이 불기 시작한다.
03	**December** 명 12월	Nancy has a plan on December 24th. Nancy는 12월 24일에 계획이 있다.
04	**midnight** 명 한밤중, 자정	Lisa goes to toilet at midnight. Lisa는 한밤중에 화장실을 간다.
05	**noon** 명 정오	It's noon already. 벌써 정오가 되었다.
06	**Sunday** 명 일요일	John takes a break on Sunday. John은 일요일에 쉰다.
07	**Monday** 명 월요일	We go to work on Monday. 우리는 월요일에 출근한다.
08	**Tuesday** 명 화요일	I have an appointment on Tuesday. 나는 화요일에 약속이 있다.
09	**Wednesday** 명 수요일	Linda always gets tired on Wednesday. Linda는 수요일에 항상 피곤해 진다.
10	**Thursday** 명 목요일	My boss will have meeting on Thursday. 나의 상사는 목요일에 회의를 가질 것이다.
11	**Friday** 명 금요일	Ailey will make a dinner Friday night. Ailey는 금요일 저녁에 저녁식사를 만들 것이다.
12	**Saturday** 명 토요일	The trip starts on Saturday, tomorrow. 그 여행은 내일 토요일에 시작한다.
13	**dollar** 명 (화폐단위) 달러	Nancy has a couple of dollars. Nancy는 몇 달러를 가지고 있다.
14	**hour** 명 시간	It takes an hour to go home from here. 여기서 집까지 가려면 1시간 걸린다.
15	**minute** 명 분	Does it takes 30minutes to cook a meal? 한 끼니를 요리하는데 30분 걸리니?

01	**put on** 동 입다, 쓰다	He puts on his favorite pants. 그는 그가 좋아하는 바지를 입는다.
02	**pull** 동 끌다, 당기다	She pulls her brothers ear. 그녀는 남동생의 귀를 당긴다.
03	**marry** 동 결혼하다	Vincent wants to marry her. Vincent는 그녀와 결혼하고 싶어 한다.
04	**favorite** 형 가장 좋아하는	This is my favorite hairband. 이것은 내가 가장 좋아하는 헤어밴드이다.
05	**kind hearted** 마음씨가 좋은	Kelly is a kind hearted girl. Kelly는 마음씨가 좋은 여자아이이다.
06	**exciting** 형 신나는, 흥미진진한	What an exciting news! 얼마나 흥미진진한 소식인지!
07	**sun block** 명 자외선 차단제	He is wearing sun block at the beach. 그는 해변가에서 자외선 차단제를 바르고 있다.
08	**wax** 동 광을 내다.	He is waxing his new car. 그는 그의 새 차에 광을 내고 있다.
09	**early bird** 부지런한 새	An early bird can eat more worms. 부지런한 새가 벌레를 좀 더 먹을 수 있다.
10	**allowance** 명 용돈	Sujin needs more allowance this month. 수진이 이번 달에 용돈이 더 필요하다.
11	**test paper** 명 시험지	Blair brings the test paper for marking. Blair는 채점하기 위해 시험지를 가져온다.
12	**take a test** 시험을 치다	We are taking a test. 우리는 시험을 치고 있다.
13	**transfer** 동 옮기다	She transfers to other school. 그녀는 다른 학교로 옮긴다.
14	**shave** 동 면도하다	My father shaves his beard every morning. 아버지는 매일 아침 (그의 수염을) 면도를 한다.
15	**businessman** 명 사업가	A businessman gives my boss a business card. 한 사업가가 나의 사장님에게 명함을 준다.

01	**then** [부] 그때	He and I was hungry then. 나와 그는 그때 배고팠다.
02	**market** [명] 시장	They go to the market. 그들은 시장에 간다.
03	**the day before yesterday** 그저께	James left here the day before yesterday. James는 그저께 여기를 떠났다.
04	**television** [명] 텔레비전	The kid is watching television. 그 아이는 텔레비전을 보고 있다.
05	**just now** 방금 전에	She left the kitchen just now. 그녀가 방금 전에 부엌을 떠났다.
06	**good-looking** [명] 잘생긴	Henry is a good-looking boy. Henry는 잘생긴 소년이다.
07	**bark** [동] 짖다	His dog barks at the postman. 그의 개는 집배원을 보고 짖는다.
08	**handmade** [형] 손으로 만든	My diary is handmade. 나의 일기는 손으로 만든 것이다.
09	**helmet** [명] 헬멧	You have to wear a helmet when you ride a bicycle. 너는 자전거를 탈 때 헬멧을 써야한다.
10	**appointment** [명] 약속	I have an appointment. 나는 약속이 있다.
11	**at that time** 그 때에	My parents were poor at that time. 내 부모님은 그 때에 가난했다.
12	**say** [동] 말하다	They are saying bad things to me. 그들은 나쁜 말들을 나에게 하고 있다.
13	**ago** [전] ~전에	We had dinner an hour ago. 우리는 1시간 전에 저녁을 먹었다.
14	**ill** [형] 아픈	Willy is ill because of the cold weather. Willy는 추운 날씨 때문에 아프다.
15	**again** [부] 다시	I want to meet you again. 나는 너를 다시 만나고 싶다.

01	**rub** 통 문지르다, 비비다	She rubbed her eyes. 그녀는 눈을 비볐다.
02	**be full of** ~로 가득하다	The bottle is full of sugar. 그 병은 설탕으로 가득하다.
03	**hairdresser** 명 미용사	Wendy wants to be a hairdresser. Wendy는 미용사가 되고 싶어한다.
04	**wallet** 명 (남성용) 지갑	The wallet is mine. 그 지갑은 내 것이다.
05	**in a row** 연속해서	Good things happen in a row these days. 요즘은 좋은 일들이 연속해서 일어난다.
06	**dead** 형 죽은	The bear was dead. 그 곰은 죽었다.
07	**liar** 명 거짓말쟁이	He is a liar to Maria. 그는 Maria에게 거짓말쟁이이다.
08	**friendly** 형 친절한	She is friendly to everyone. 그녀는 모두에게 친절하다.
09	**forest** 명 숲	Judy plants a tree in the forest every year. Judy는 그 숲에 매년 나무 한 그루 심는다.
10	**nail shop** 명 네일샵	Tom doesn't go to nail shop. Tom은 네일샵에 가지 않는다.
11	**volleyball** 명 배구	He is in the volleyball team. 그는 배구팀에 속해 있다.
12	**voice** 명 목소리	The actress's voice on the movie is nice. 그 영화의 여배우의 목소리는 좋다.
13	**scribble** 통 낙서하다	We scribble on the school's wall. 우리는 학교의 벽에 낙서한다.
14	**school supplies** 명 학용품	He brings school supplies on the way to schoo 그는 학교 가는 길에 학용품을 가져간다.
15	**sign up** 등록하다	He signs up the yoga class. 그는 요가 수업을 등록한다.

01	**think** 동 생각하다	Kelly thinks that the storm broke the window. Kelly는 폭풍이 그 창문을 깨뜨렸다고 생각한다.
02	**make a reservation** 예약하다	I made a reservation yesterday. 나는 어제 예약을 했다.
03	**at one time** 한때	John was a university student at one time. John은 한때 대학교 학생이었다.
04	**on vacation** 휴가 중	He is on vacation until the end of the month. 그는 월 말까지 휴가 중이다.
05	**seat** 명 자리	The man's seat is close from me. 그 남자의 자리는 나와 가깝다.
06	**feel a chill** 한기를 느끼다	My son feels a chill suddenly. 나의 아들은 갑자기 한기를 느낀다.
07	**drop** 동 떨어뜨리다	My mother dropped her earing into the hole. 내 어머니는 그 구멍에 그녀의 귀걸이를 떨어뜨렸다.
08	**close** 형 가까운	Mary is my close neighbor Mary는 나의 가까운 이웃이다.
09	**crust** 명 겉껍질	Chris doesn't eat bread crust. Chris는 빵껍질을 먹지 않는다.
10	**hammer** 명 망치	His wife is finding her hammer. 그의 아내는 그녀의 망치를 찾고 있다.
11	**bat** 명 박쥐	Ms. Smith saw many bats in the cave. Ms. Smith는 그 동굴에서 많은 박쥐를 보았다.
12	**hurry up** 서두르다	Rina hurries up before going to school. Rina는 학교 가기 전에 서두른다.
13	**riddle** 명 수수께끼	Lisa solves riddles very well. Lisa는 수수께끼를 매우 잘 푼다.
14	**alive** 형 살아있는	This frog is alive. 이 개구리는 살아있다.
15	**essay** 명 수필	Yujin wrote an essay about Korean food. 유진은 한국음식에 대해 수필을 썼다.

Unit 05

01	**walk a dog** 개를 산책시키다	We walk our dog. 우리는 우리의 개를 산책시킨다.
02	**printer** 명 프린터	Did he use the printer? 그는 그 프린터를 사용했니?
03	**ice rink** 명 스케이트장	Linda and I go to ice rink in Winter. Linda와 나는 겨울에 스케이트장을 간다.
04	**carpet** 명 양탄자, 카펫	I'll buy a new carpet. 나는 새 카펫을 살 것이다.
05	**toaster** 명 토스터	The girl is heating the bread with a toaster. 그 소녀는 토스터로 빵을 데우고 있다.
06	**doorway** 명 출입구	I am standing in front of a doorway. 나는 출입구 앞에 서있다.
07	**tongue** 명 혀	His tongue stuck on the ice cream. 그의 혀는 아이스크림에 붙었다.
08	**hold one's tongue** 잠자코 있다	We held our tongue at the moment. 우리는 그때 잠자코 있었다.
09	**break time** 명 휴식 시간	Henry doesn't have break time while working. Henry는 일할 때 휴식 시간을 가지지 않는다.
10	**in the air** 공중에서	The airplane is flying in the air. 그 비행기는 공중에서 날고 있다.
11	**cough** 동 기침하다	She coughs in front of me. 그녀는 내 앞에서 기침을 한다.
12	**corner** 명 구석	Sandy sits at the corner of the class. Sandy는 그 반의 구석에 앉는다.
13	**surf in the Internet** 인테넷 검색을 하다	Jamy surfs in the Internet to find some data. Jamy는 자료를 찾기 위해 인터넷 검색을 한다.
14	**greeting** 명 인사	He waves his hand in greeting me. 그는 그의 손을 흔들어 나에게 인사를 한다.
15	**give a speech** 연설하다	My father gave a speech for many students. 나의 아버지는 많은 학생들을 위해 연설을 하였다.

01 make a fire
불을 지피다
The man made a fire at the camp.
그 남자는 캠프에서 불을 지폈다.

02 instead of
~대신에
I voted for Mike instead of Sandy.
나는 Sandy 대신 Mike에게 투표를 했다.

03 visitor
® 방문자
The visitor saw the building.
그 방문자는 그 건물을 보았다.

04 make one's bed
침대를 정리하다
She makes her bed before she leaves her room.
그녀는 그녀의 방을 떠나기 전에 침대를 정리한다.

05 set the alarm clock
알람시계를 맞추다
John sets the alarm clock to wake up early.
John은 일찍 일어나기 위해 알람시계를 맞춘다.

06 sneakers
® 운동화
He lost his sneakers.
그는 그의 운동화를 잃어버렸다.

07 do the laundry
빨래하다
The boy did the laundry before evening.
그 소년은 저녁 전에 빨래를 했다.

08 deli
® 델리, 식품점
Mary buys some salad from the deli.
Mary는 델리에서 샐러드를 좀 산다.

09 celebrity
® 연예인
He became a celebrity after the TV show.
그는 그 TV쇼 이후 연예인이 되었다.

10 lean on
기대다
Susan leans on my shoulder.
Susan은 나의 어깨에 기댄다.

11 marathon
® 마라톤 대회
Mary runs for the marathon every year.
Mary는 매년 마라톤 대회를 달린다.

12 guidebook
® 안내 책자
She looks through the guidebook.
그녀는 안내 책자를 훑어본다.

13 wedding cake
® 웨딩 케이크
I made a wedding cake for the party.
나는 그 파티를 위해 웨딩케이크를 준비했다.

14 machine
® 기계
The doctor made a walking machine.
그 박사는 걷는 기계를 만들었다.

15 director
® 감독, 지도자
He was a director.
그는 감독이었다.

01	**invite** 동 초대하다	Jane invites her classmates to the party. Jane은 파티에 그녀의 반 친구들을 초대한다.
02	**take a photo** 사진을 찍다	She takes a photo of her son. 그녀는 그녀의 아들의 사진을 찍는다.
03	**landscape** 명 풍경화, 풍경	They are watching the landscape. 그들은 풍경화를 보고 있다.
04	**soon** 부 곧	The tutor will arrive soon. 그 과외 선생님은 곧 도착할 것이다.
05	**compose** 동 작곡하다	Tim composed a song for her mother. Tim은 그의 어머니를 위해 노래를 작곡했다.
06	**school materials** 명 학교 준비물	I forgot to bring the school materials. 나는 학교 준비물을 가져오는걸 잊었다.
07	**skip** 동 건너뛰다	The director skips a scene. 그 감독은 장면 하나를 건너뛴다.
08	**hunter** 명 사냥꾼	They are hunters. 그들은 사냥꾼이다.
09	**mind** 명 마음, 정신	He opened his mind. 그는 마음을 열었다.
10	**disappear** 동 사라지다	She disappears at lunch time. 그녀는 점심시간에 사라진다.
11	**in the future** 미래에	You want to be a star in the future. 너는 미래에 스타가 되고 싶어 한다.
12	**judge** 명 판사	Peter met the judge at the restaurant. Peter는 그 레스토랑에서 판사를 만났다.
13	**plant** 명 식물	Do you grow any plant in your house? 너는 집에서 식물을 기르니?
14	**wealth** 명 부, 재산	She always cares about her wealth. 그녀는 언제나 자신의 부에 대해 신경 쓴다.
15	**magazine** 명 잡지	Matt reads magazine every month. Matt은 매달 잡지를 읽는다.

01	**campfire** 명 모닥불	The campfire makes us warm. 모닥불은 우리를 따뜻하게 만들어 준다.
02	**diet** 명 식이요법, 다이어트	Jane was on a diet at that time. Jane은 그때 다이어트를 하고 있었다.
03	**take a message** 메모를 받다	Can you take a message for me? 나를 위해 메모를 받아줄래요?
04	**cost** 통 비용이 들다	It costs almost 10 dollars to fix the radio. 그 라디오를 고치기 위해 거의 10달러가 들었다.
05	**copy** 통 복사하다	Willy copies my note after class. Willy는 수업 후에 내 노트를 복사한다.
06	**race** 명 경주	Is your horse in the race? 너의 말은 경주에 참가하니?
07	**paint** 통 페인트 칠 하다	Chris paints the small room for his baby. Chris는 그의 아기를 위해 그 작은 방을 칠한다.
08	**Swiss** 명 스위스	He and I want to climb a mountain in Swiss. 그와 나는 스위스에서 산을 오르고 싶어 한다.
09	**bank** 명 은행	My uncle caught a thief at the bank. 삼촌은 그 은행에서 도둑을 잡았다.
10	**cherry** 명 체리	Jimmy puts some cherries on the cake. Jimmy는 그 케이크 위에 몇 개의 체리를 놓는다.
11	**Europe** 명 유럽	I traveled in Europe. 나는 유럽을 여행했다.
12	**jump rope** 명 줄넘기	She exercises with a jump rope. 그녀는 줄넘기로 운동한다.
13	**hotel** 명 호텔	They are staying at the hotel. 그들은 호텔에서 지내고 있다.
14	**toss** 통 (가볍게) 던지다	I toss the ball to another player. 나는 다른 선수에게 공을 던진다.
15	**boots** 명 부츠	Mr. Morris wears the boots at the farm. Mr. Morris는 농장에서 부츠를 신는다.

| 01 | **puppy**
몡 강아지 | They have cute puppies.
그들은 귀여운 강아지들이 있다. |

| 02 | **perform**
통 공연하다 | The man performs magic tricks on the stage.
그 남자는 무대에서 마술 공연을 한다. |

| 03 | **Russia**
몡 러시아 | Is he from Russia?
그는 러시아에서 출신이니? |

| 04 | **curry and rice**
몡 카레라이스 | His mother makes curry and rice for dinner.
그의 어머니는 저녁으로 카레라이스를 만든다. |

| 05 | **fashionable**
혱 유행하는 | The model has a lot of fashionable clothes.
그 모델은 유행하는 옷을 많이 가지고 있다. |

| 06 | **stew**
몡 스튜 | I bought some stew from the restaurant.
나는 그 레스토랑에서 스튜를 좀 샀다. |

| 07 | **hole**
몡 구멍 | Mr. Williams made a hole on the box.
Mr. Williams는 상자에 구멍을 냈다. |

| 08 | **America**
몡 미국 | America is a powerful country.
미국은 강한 나라이다. |

| 09 | **movie**
몡 영화 | Catherine watches a movie alone.
Catherine은 혼자 영화를 본다. |

| 10 | **fine**
혱 좋은, 화창한 | What a fine day it is!
날씨가 정말 화창하구나! |

| 11 | **poetry**
몡 시 | The poetry is very beautiful.
그 시는 매우 아름답다. |

| 12 | **Japanese**
몡 일본의, 일본어 | She can speak Japanese well.
그녀는 일본어를 잘한다. |

| 13 | **hike**
몡 하이킹 (도보여행)을 하다 | The boys hike 10miles every month.
그 남자아이들은 매달 10마일씩 도보여행을 한다. |

| 14 | **oil**
몡 기름 | It's difficult to cook without oil.
기름 없이 요리하는 것은 어렵다. |

| 15 | **skinny**
혱 마른 | Her arms are too skinny.
그녀의 팔은 너무 말랐다. |

01	**unkind** 형 불친절한	Dylan is sometimes unkind to me. Dylan은 가끔 불친절하다.
02	**thick** 형 두꺼운	The dictionaries are very thick. 그 사전들은 매우 두껍다.
03	**proud** 형 자랑스러워 하는	Susan is proud of the result. Susan은 그 결과에 대해 자랑스러워한다.
04	**golfer** 명 골프 치는 사람	The golfers are standing on the grass. 그 골퍼들이 잔디위에 서있다.
05	**drama** 명 드라마	Billy watches a drama at night. Billy는 밤에 드라마를 본다.
06	**report** 명 보고서	The man is typing a report. 그 남자는 보고서를 타자치고 있다.
07	**quiet** 명 조용한	She is very quiet all the time. 그녀는 항상 조용하다.
08	**large** 형 커다란	She has a large garden. 그녀는 커다란 정원을 가지고 있다.
09	**tower** 명 탑	Jimmy goes to the top of the tower. Jimmy는 그 탑의 꼭대기에 오른다.
10	**get out of** 빠져나오다	How do we get out of this crowd? 우리는 이 군중들에서 어떻게 빠져나가지?
11	**clerk** 명 점원	There are 50 clerks in that department store. 저 백화점에는 50명의 점원이 있다.
12	**melon** 명 멜론	Kelly serves some melons to her guests. Kelly는 그녀의 손님들에게 약간의 멜론을 대접한다.
13	**cartoon book** 명 만화책	My father hates cartoon books. 내 아버지는 만화책을 싫어하신다.
14	**sharp** 형 뾰족한, 날카로운	Sharks have sharp teeth. 상어들은 날카로운 이빨을 가지고 있다.
15	**motion** 명 동작	What a funny motion it is! 그 동작이 얼마나 웃긴지!

01	**nurse** 몡 간호사	Jane is a nurse at the hospital. Jane은 그 병원의 간호사이다.
02	**by** 젠 전. 까지	I have to turn in my homework by Monday. 나는 월요일까지 숙제를 제출해야한다.
03	**sweet potato** 몡 고구마	The horse bites a sweet potato. 그 말이 고구마를 베어 문다.
04	**kangaroo** 몡 캥거루	Kangaroos live in Australia. 캥거루는 호주에 산다.
05	**pick up** ~를 차에 태우다	His friend picked me up after work. 그의 친구는 퇴근 후 나를 차에 태웠다.
06	**schoolbag** 몡 책가방	My schoolbag is pink. 나의 책가방은 분홍색이다.
07	**plaza** 몡 광장	Jake hangs out with his classmates at the plaza. Jake는 그의 반 친구들과 광장에서 논다.
08	**storekeeper** 몡 가게 주인	She is a storekeeper. 그녀는 가게 주인이다.
09	**silent** 혱 조용한	My daughter is sleeping in the silent room. 나의 딸은 조용한 방에서 자고 있다.
10	**Italy** 몡 이탈리아	Italy is famous for pizza. 이탈리아는 피자로 유명하다.
11	**all** 혱 모든	She loves all children. 그녀는 모든 아이들을 사랑한다.
12	**fact** 몡 사실	She is telling the fact to the policeman. 그녀는 경찰에게 사실을 이야기하고 있다.
13	**Canada** 몡 캐나다	Kathy is from Canada. Kathy는 Canada 출신이다.
14	**sentence** 몡 문장	Do you understand the sentence? 그 문장을 이해하니?
15	**gun** 몡 총	The hunters have guns. 그 사냥꾼들은 총을 가지고 있다.

01	**flower pot** 명 화분	Amy planted a seed in the flower pot. Amy는 화분에 씨를 심었다.
02	**light** 명 빛, 전등	Turn off all the lights. 모든 전등을 꺼라.
03	**dining room** 명 (집안의) 식당	We were in the dining room. 우리는 식당에 있었다.
04	**skirt** 명 치마	Danny chose a skirt for his mother. Danny는 그의 어머니를 위해 치마를 골랐다.
05	**golfer** 명 골프 치는 사람	The golfers are standing on the grass. 그 골퍼들은 잔디위에 서있다.
06	**fireworks** 명 불꽃놀이	Let's go to see the fireworks. 같이 불꽃놀이를 보러 가자.
07	**clothes** 명 옷	Mr. Smith doesn't wash his clothes often. Smith씨는 그의 옷을 자주 세탁하지 않는다.
08	**neighbor** 명 이웃	My neighbor grows a horse at the farm. 나의 이웃은 그 농장에서 말을 키운다.
09	**Paris** 명 파리, 프랑스의 수도	We lived in Paris then. 우리는 그때 파리에 살았다.
10	**tulip** 명 튤립	Look at this tulip! 이 튤립을 봐!
11	**uniform** 명 제복, 유니폼	Show me your uniform. 너의 유니폼을 보여줘.
12	**plastic** 명 플라스틱	It is a plastic box. 그것은 플라스틱 상자이다.
13	**French fries** 명 감자튀김	I have some French fries. 나는 감자튀김을 먹는다.
14	**quickly** 부 빨리	My son cleans his room quickly. 아들은 그의 방을 빨리 청소 하였다.
15	**same** 형 같은	The customer buys the same item with her partner. 그 손님은 그녀의 파트너와 같은 제품을 산다.

다음 우리말 뜻에 맞는 영어 단어를 쓰시오.

01 구성원

02 달러

03 끝나다

04 (건물의) 층, 바닥

05 방향, 지시

06 탄산음료

07 손가락

08 둘러싸다

09 ~의 나이에

10 중학교

11 결혼기념일

12 독후감

13 학년

14 쇼핑센터

15 비자

다음 우리말 뜻에 맞는 영어 단어를 쓰시오.

01 시청

02 정물

03 월세

04 라면을 끓이다

05 자명종

06 철자를 말하다

07 횡단보도

08 진찰을 받다

09 강도

10 소나무

11 점, (뾰족한) 끝

12 답장하다

13 뒤쫓다

14 외계인

15 모래성

다음 우리말 뜻에 맞는 영어 단어를 쓰시오.

01 백

02 천

03 4분의 1, 15분, 25센트

04 2분의 1, 절반, 30분

05 지나간

06 (한) 달

07 1월

08 2월

09 3월

10 4월

11 5월

12 6월

13 7월

14 8월

15 9월

다음 우리말 뜻에 맞는 영어 단어를 쓰시오.

01 10월

02 11월

03 12월

04 자정

05 정오

06 일요일

07 월요일

08 화요일

09 수요일

10 목요일

11 금요일

12 토요일

13 (화폐단위) 달러

14 시간

15 분

다음 우리말 뜻에 맞는 영어 단어를 쓰시오.

01 사업가

02 옮기다

03 시험지

04 부지런한 새

05 자외선 차단제

06 면도하다

07 시험을 치다

08 용돈

09 광을 내다

10 신나는, 흥미진진한

11 가장 좋아하는

12 당기다

13 마음씨가 좋은

14 결혼하다

15 입다, 쓰다

다음 우리말 뜻에 맞는 영어 단어를 쓰시오.

01 다시

02 ~전에

03 그 때에

04 헬멧

05 짖다

06 아픈

07 말하다

08 약속

09 손으로 만든

10 잘생긴

11 텔레비전

12 시장

13 방금 전에

14 그저께

15 그때

Quiz

다음 우리말 뜻에 맞는 영어 단어를 쓰시오.

01 등록하다

02 낙서하다

03 배구

04 숲

05 거짓말쟁이

06 학용품

07 목소리

08 네일샵

09 친절한

10 죽은

11 (남성용) 지갑

12 ~로 가득하다

13 연속해서

14 미용사

15 문지르다

다음 우리말 뜻에 맞는 영어 단어를 쓰시오.

01　수필

02　수수께끼

03　박쥐

04　겉껍질

05　떨어뜨리다

06　살아있는

07　서두르다

08　망치

09　가까운

10　한기를 느끼다

11　휴가 중

12　예약하다

13　자리

14　한때

15　생각하다

다음 우리말 뜻에 맞는 영어 단어를 쓰시오.

01 연설하다

02 인터넷에서 검색을 하다

03 기침하다

04 잠자코 있다

05 혀

06 인사

07 구석

08 공중에서

09 휴식 시간

10 출입구

11 양탄자

12 프린터

13 토스터

14 스케이트장

15 개를 산책시키다

다음 우리말 뜻에 맞는 영어 단어를 쓰시오.

01 감독, 지도자

02 결혼 케이크

03 마라톤 대회

04 연예인

05 빨래하다

06 기계

07 안내 책자

08 ~에 기대다

09 델리, 식품점

10 운동화

11 침대를 정리하다

12 ~ 대신에

13 알람을 맞추다

14 방문자

15 불을 지피다

다음 우리말 뜻에 맞는 영어 단어를 쓰시오.

01 잡지

02 식물

03 건너뛰다

04 마음, 정신

05 미래에

06 부, 재산

07 판사

08 사라지다

09 사냥꾼

10 학교 준비물

11 곧

12 사진을 찍다

13 작곡하다

14 풍경화, 풍경

15 초대하다

다음 우리말 뜻에 맞는 영어 단어를 쓰시오.

01 부츠

02 호텔

03 유럽

04 은행

05 페인트 칠 하다

06 (가볍게) 던지다

07 줄넘기

08 체리

09 복사하다

10 경주

11 비용이 들다

12 다이어트

13 스위스

14 메모를 받다

15 모닥불

다음 우리말 뜻에 맞는 영어 단어를 쓰시오.

01 마른

02 도보여행 (하이킹)을 하다

03 시

04 영화

05 구멍

06 기름

07 일본어

08 화창한

09 미국

10 스튜

11 카레라이스

12 공연하다

13 유행하는

14 러시아

15 강아지

다음 우리말 뜻에 맞는 영어 단어를 쓰시오.

01 동작

02 뾰족한, 날카로운

03 멜론

04 탑

05 커다란

06 만화책

07 점원

08 빠져나오다

09 조용한

10 보고서

11 골프 치는 사람

12 두꺼운

13 드라마

14 자랑스러워 하는

15 불친절한

다음 우리말 뜻에 맞는 영어 단어를 쓰시오.

01 총

02 캐나다

03 모든

04 조용한

05 광장

06 문장

07 사실

08 이탈리아

09 가게 주인

10 책가방

11 캥거루

12 전, 까지

13 ~를 차에 태우다

14 고구마

15 간호사

다음 우리말 뜻에 맞는 영어 단어를 쓰시오.

01 같은

02 감자 튀김

03 제복

04 (도시) 파리, 프랑스의 수도

05 옷

06 빨리

07 플라스틱

08 튤립

09 이웃

10 불꽃놀이

11 치마

12 전등

13 골프치는 사람

14 (집안의) 식당

15 화분

Answer **KEY**

Unit 01

1회 01 member 02 dollar 03 be over
04 floor 05 direction 06 soft drink
07 finger 08 surround 09 at the age of
10 middle school 11 wedding day
12 book report 13 grade 14 mall
15 visa

2회 01 City Hall 02 still object
03 monthly rent 04 make ramen
05 alarm clock 06 spell 07 crosswalk
08 see a doctor 09 robber 10 pine tree
11 point 12 write in answer 13 run after
14 E.T 15 sand castle

Unit 02

1회 01 hundred 02 thousand
03 quarter 04 half 05 past 06 month
07 January 08 February 09 March
10 April 11 May 12 June 13 July
14 August 15 September

2회 01 October 02 November
03 December 04 midnight 05 noon
06 Sunday 07 Monday 08 Tuesday
09 Wednesday 10 Thursday 11 Friday
12 Saturday 13 dollar 14 hour
15 minute

Unit 03

1회 01 businessman 02 transfer
03 test paper 04 early bird 05 sun block
06 shave 07 take a test 08 allowance
09 wax 10 exciting 11 favorite 12 pull
13 kind hearted 14 marry 15 put on

2회 01 again 02 ago 03 at that time
04 helmet 05 bark 06 ill 07 say
08 appointment 09 hand-made
10 good-looking 11 television 12 market
13 just now 14 the day before yesterday
15 then

Unit 04

1회 01 sign up 02 scribble 03 volleyball
04 forest 05 liar 06 school supply
07 voice 08 nail shop 09 friendly
10 dead 11 wallet 12 be full with
13 in a row 14 hairdresser 15 rub

2회 01 essay 02 riddle 03 bat
04 crust 05 drop 06 alive 07 hurry up
08 hammer 09 close 10 feel a chill
11 on vacation 12 make a reservation
13 seat 14 at one time 15 think

Unit 05

1회 01 give a speech 02 surf in the Internet 03 cough 04 hold one's tongue 05 tongue 06 greeting 07 corner 08 in the air 09 breaktime 10 doorway 11 carpet 12 printer 13 toaster 14 ice rink 15 walk a dog

2회 01 director 02 wedding cake 03 marathon 04 celebrity 05 do the laundry 06 machine 07 guidebook 08 lean on 09 deli 10 sneakers 11 make one's bed 12 instead of 13 set the alarm clock 14 visitor 15 make a fire

Unit 06

1회 01 magazine 02 plant 03 skip 04 mind 05 in the future 06 wealth 07 judge 08 disappear 09 hunter 10 school materials 11 soon 12 take a photo 13 compose 14 landscape 15 invite

2회 01 boots 02 hotel 03 Europe 04 bank 05 paint 06 toss 07 jump rope 08 cherry 09 copy 10 race 11 cost 12 diet 13 Swiss 14 take a message 15 campfire

Unit 07

1회 01 skinny 02 hike 03 poetry 04 movie 05 hole 06 oil 07 Japanese 08 fine 09 America 10 stew 11 curry and rice 12 perform 13 fashionable 14 Russia 15 puppy

2회 01 motion 02 sharp 03 melon 04 tower 05 large 06 cartoon book 07 clerk 08 get out of 09 quiet 10 report 11 golfer 12 thick 13 drama 14 proud 15 unkind

Unit 08

1회 01 gun 02 Canada 03 all 04 silent 05 plaza 06 sentence 07 fact 08 Italy 09 storekeeper 10 schoolbag 11 kangaroo 12 by 13 pick up 14 sweet potato 15 nurse

2회 01 same 02 French fries 03 uniform 04 Paris 05 clothes 06 quickly 07 plastic 08 tulip 09 neighbor 10 fireworks 11 skirt 12 light 13 golfer 14 dining room 15 flower pot